the Diabetes cookbook

D1441752

THE AUSTRALIAN
Women's Weekly

contents

In Australia, thousands of people are diagnosed with type-2 (adult-onset) diabetes every year. It's a deadly disease, but the good news is, it's preventable in most cases. The team in The Australian Women's Weekly Test Kitchen have come up with everyday recipes that are tasty, easy to prepare, well-balanced and have been nutritionally assessed and counted. If you follow the guidelines and recipes in this cookbook, and embark on a regular exercise regime, your health and well-being will benefit enormously.

Pamela Clark

Food Director

the diabetes epidemic

It's estimated that one person develops diabetes in Australia every 10 minutes. This is a staggering figure, especially when a large number of type-2 diabetes cases can be prevented by exercise and a healthy diet.

Type-2 diabetes used to be called adult-onset diabetes because it mainly affected people in their 50s or older. But now, teenagers and people in their 20s have begun to be diagnosed with type-2 diabetes. There is no cure, but eating healthily and exercising moderately will go a long way towards keeping it under control. This book of delicious low-fat recipes will help you keep your weight down and, if you eat like this as a way of life, you'll greatly reduce your risk of ever developing diabetes.

A diet with enough food and kilojoules to obtain or maintain a healthy body weight, low in fat (particularly saturated fat) and high in fresh unprocessed food, coupled with a reasonable amount of physical activity, is generally regarded as a straightforward and simple guide to a healthy life. Such a regime will not only help you maintain a proper weight, it can also help keep your cholesterol and blood pressure levels under control and assist in reducing the risk of heart disease and type-2 diabetes.

While genetics and lifestyle play a part in determining a person's weight, the fact remains that too many of us eat badly. Witness the growth in the takeaway and fast food industries, the increase in the percentage of people who can be classed as overweight or obese, and the growing incidence of type-2 diabetes and heart disease. High saturated-fat intakes have been linked not only to both of these diseases but to certain types of cancer as well.

the old days vs the present

In the distant past, our ancestors lived on a diet – consisting primarily of grains, cereals, fruits, vegetables, nuts and legumes – that was relatively low in saturated fat and high in foods that promoted activity. Our ancestors were very active and did not consume the quantity of food that we do today. Our diet, however, has evolved into one in which large serving sizes, saturated fats and overprocessed foods rule; it's a menu tailored to increase body weight and both our blood glucose (sugar) and insulin levels to worrying heights. Pressed for time and blessed with science, we rely heavily on foods that are quick to get to the table and don't need a lot of preparation. Worse, some manufactured and many takeaway foods use large quantities of fat and kilojoules to make bland carbohydrates exciting – think of deep-frying for potatoes.

carbohydrates

In tandem with lowering our saturated fat intakes, we should also concentrate on consuming more carbohydrates. Carbohydrate foods generally make us feel fuller faster than do fats, give us more energy, help stave off hunger pangs and do not easily convert to body fat. But what are they?

Carbohydrates come mostly from plants, ie., cereals and grains, fruits, vegetables and legumes, but dairy products also contain carbohydrates. Recommended dietary guidelines suggest we eat substantial servings of cereals, legumes, rice and pasta, followed by vegetables and fruits. Dairy products should be eaten in moderation then, in diminishing quantities, meat, sugar, butter and the like can be consumed. People with diabetes are recommended to evenly distribute their carbohydrate intake in three meals throughout the day.

the glycaemic index

While a high-carbohydrate diet is better for us than a high-fat diet, some research suggests that certain kinds of carbohydrate foods are better than others. During the 1980s, nutritional research resulted in the creation of the glycaemic index (GI), a ranking of carbohydrates in foods based on their impact on blood glucose (sugar) levels in the body. Originally developed to help people with diabetes, research is showing that the GI may be a valid tool to assist in weight loss and heart disease prevention.

Rapidly absorbed pure glucose has a GI of 100. Carbohydrates that break down slowly and release glucose into the blood stream gradually have low GI values (55 or less), while those that are easily digested and absorbed quickly are considered to have high GI values (70 or more).

Medium (or intermediate) GI foods have values between 55 and 70. Low-fat high-GI food doesn't have to be excluded from a healthy diet – when coupled with equal amounts of low-GI food the result is a healthy diet with an intermediate-GI rating. The most important rule to follow is to eat as wide a variety as possible of low-saturated fat, low-to-medium GI foods.

fibre

Dietary fibre is mainly indigestible plant matter that has no nutritional value. Unable to be absorbed, it acts as roughage to help keep the digestive system healthy and filter excess cholesterol from digestive juices – essential in the maintenance of healthy gut bacteria. High-fibre carbohydrates as a rule have lower GI values and help assuage hunger pangs. A diet high in fibre is beneficial for people with type-2 diabetes, and nutritionists advise that a healthy diet includes at least 30g of fibre daily. Good fibre sources are wholegrain cereals, brans and breads, and unpeeled, raw fruits and vegetables.

high-carbohydrate foods

- Bread, especially wholegrain and wholemeal varieties
- Crispbreads and crackers
- High-fibre breakfast cereals, including rolled oats, whole wheat and untoasted muesli
- Pasta and rice (such as basmati or Doongara)
- Other grains such as barley, bulgur and couscous
- Legumes, including baked beans, kidney beans, chickpeas, lentils, three bean mix
- Fruit (also a good source of fibre if the whole fruit is eaten, rather than juiced)
- Low-fat milk products, including milk, soy drinks
- Starchy vegetables, such as potatoes, sweet potato, yams, sweet corn

reduce bad fats

- Choose reduced or low-fat dairy foods (milk, yogurt, ice-cream, custard)
- Choose lean meat; trim any excess fat from meat before cooking
- Remove skin from chicken
- Avoid using fats that are solid at room temperature. These contain saturated fat, also known as "bad" fat, which increases your LDL cholesterol level
- Limit the amount of cheese, or choose low-fat or reduced-fat varieties
- Limit processed deli meats
- Avoid fried takeaway foods

enjoy healthy fats

- Stir-fry meat and vegetables in a little canola oil, or use a cooking-oil spray or a little water
- Don't use creamy dressings on salads, instead dress with a vinaigrette made with a little olive oil and lemon juice or vinegar
- Spread avocado on sandwiches and toast, or add to a salad
- Eat fish at least three times a week. They contain omega-3, a type of fat that is good for your heart
- Top pastas with tomato-based sauces instead of creamy sauces

fats

Eating too much saturated fat is bad for your health – it raises blood cholesterol more than other forms of fat and has far more kilojoules than carbohydrates or protein. High levels of saturated fat in the diet are linked to an increased risk of heart and vascular disease, and certain cancers. The reason we consume saturated fat at all is because it is unavoidable in meat, many dairy products and some vegetable oils; its benefits are that it carries fat-soluble vitamins (A, D, E and K), it provides energy and supplies certain essential fatty acids needed to maintain the structure of cell membranes and form hormone-like substances that regulate the body's biochemistry. It is best for healthy adults to reduce daily consumption of saturated fats to less than 8 per cent of total kilojoule intake. Saturated fats (known as "bad" fats) tend to be solid at room temperature and are found mainly in animal products such as butter, cream, chicken skin, fat on meat, cheese, lard and dripping. They are also found in pies and cakes, snack foods, pastries and oils such as palm and coconut.

Polyunsaturated fat is mainly found in plant foods, including sunflower, soy bean and safflower oils and nuts and seeds. It is also found in oily fish, such as salmon, tuna and sardines. Omega-3 and omega-6 fatty acids are types of polyunsaturated fats; omega-3 fats are mainly found in fish and omega-6 fats are mainly found in vegetable oils. Polyunsaturated fats (known as "good" fats) are liquid at room temperature, and can help lower blood cholesterol and reduce the risk of cardiovascular disease.

Monounsaturated fat is found in oils including canola and olive oils, and other plant foods including avocados, nuts and seeds, as well as in lean meat. They are generally liquid at room temperature, but may solidify in cold temperatures. These fats, another type of "good" fat, can help lower blood cholesterol and reduce the risk of cardiovascular disease.

Regardless of whether fat is good or bad, *all* fat contributes to weight gain and, in addition to reducing the amount of "bad" fat eaten, overweight people with type-2 diabetes also need to reduce the total amount of fat they eat.

sugar

A healthy eating plan for people with diabetes can include some sugar without it adversely affecting diabetes control and weight management. However, it's still important to consider the nutritional value of the foods you eat. Added sugars in nutritious foods, such as breakfast cereals or low-fat dairy products, are preferable to foods or drinks, such as confectionary and soft drinks, that contain little or no nutritional benefits but plenty of kilojoules. Many recipes can also be modified to use less than the stated amount of sugar.

Alternative sweeteners are available and, while it's no longer necessary to always use these instead of natural sugar, they are still useful in foods that may be consumed in large amounts, such as cordials and soft drinks. Some alternative sweeteners are low kilojoule or kilojoule-free and will not significantly affect blood glucose levels, however, this is not true for all alternative sweeteners, especially those known as nutritive or carbohydrate-modified sweeteners; these are not kilojoule-free and can effect blood glucose levels, so care must be taken.

sodium

It's a given that we should all eat less salt (sodium); it can lead to increased blood pressure and the accompanying risk of heart disease and stroke. Still, sodium is essential in our diet – the recommended daily intake is 920mg to 2300mg, but this level can be achieved through the salt found naturally in fresh foods and unavoidably in manufactured foods. Try to choose processed foods that are labelled "no added salt" or "salt-reduced", and similarly try to avoid highly salted foods such as potato chips, salted nuts and most takeaway foods. Instead of using salt at the table, flavour your food with cracked pepper, chopped fresh herbs, lemon juice or balsamic vinegar, garlic, chilli and the like. Make your own mustard, tomato sauce, chutney and sweet chilli sauce – without adding salt. Use dried ground spices, onions and leeks, wine and vinegar in cooking instead of salt.

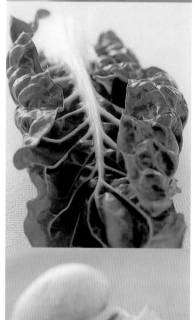

eat your vegies

• An apple a day may keep the doctor away, but for keeping well and having a sense of wellbeing, turn to vegetables… five servings a day is the recommended amount. Recent studies indicate that phytochemicals (naturally occurring plant chemicals) and antioxidants (elements that stop free radicals from destroying DNA) contained in vegetables can play a part in reducing the possibility of cancer and heart disease.

• Eat more tomatoes (a good source of vitamin C), spinach (loaded with B vitamins, iron and folate) and broccoli (rich in fibre and calcium). Keep washed and trimmed celery, carrot, fennel, cucumber and the like in the refrigerator; you're more likely to snack on them if they're ready to eat. Juice vegetables when they look a little tired.

• Serve a green salad with every main meal – keep it simple so it's less of a chore to make. Use fresh lemon juice or balsamic vinegar and finely chopped herbs for a dressing.

• Make fresh pasta sauces from vegetables – the Italians have done so for centuries. Broccoli or cauliflower florets, sugar snap or snow peas, chopped red onion, sliced mushrooms, cherry tomatoes or finely shaved fennel can be tossed into just-drained hot pasta and eaten immediately.

• Think about roasting or grilling your vegetables. Carrots, pumpkin, kumara, yams, turnips and beetroot can all be roasted in a hot oven and are perfectly delicious without adding anything to them. And eggplant, capsicum, zucchini and whole red onions are delectable grilled on a hotplate or the barbecue.

• Don't forget how good homemade vegetable soup is, or how easy it is to make a vegie stir-fry with lots of chilli, ginger and garlic.

• We are blessed with a wide variety of vegetables available in our supermarkets and greengrocers – so work your way through the huge selection. There's nothing wrong with eating the same old standards year in year out, but trying different vegetables can make meals more interesting. Select those in season, when they're at their peak.

7-day menu planner

	breakfast	lunch	dinner	dessert
monday	Rolled oat porridge (p14) *plus* 1 slice wholegrain bread *plus* 1 apple	Cottage cheese and salad on 2 slices of multigrain bread *plus* 1 orange	Crisp-skinned snapper with stir-fried vegetables and black beans (p50) *plus* 1 cup cooked brown rice	½ papaya sprinkled with lime juice
tuesday	2 crumpets with unsaturated margarine or Vegemite *plus* 1 small tub low-fat fruit yogurt	Chilli and lime chicken salad (p41) *plus* 1 apple *plus* 2 slices wholegrain bread	Lentil cottage pie (p61) *plus* a green salad	½ cup sliced strawberries served with the pulp of one passionfruit
wednesday	Untoasted muesli (p25) *plus* 1 banana	1 cup canned peaches in natural juice *plus* 1 small tub low-fat yogurt (any flavour) *plus* 1 cup orange juice	Rosemary, brie and sun-dried tomato chicken on corn mash (p48) *plus* steamed broccoli and carrots	1 small can unsweetened two fruits *plus* 1 scoop low-fat ice-cream (any flavour)
thursday	Citrus compote (p21) *plus* 2 slices toasted multigrain bread with unsaturated margarine	Kumara and coriander soup (p30) *plus* 1 wholemeal bread roll	Herb-crusted lamb racks with kipfler potatoes and leek (p57) *plus* steamed brussels sprouts	Yogurt and mango jelly (p110)
friday	Morning trifles (p25) *plus* 2 slices toasted wholemeal bread with Vegemite or unsaturated margarine	Rice and chickpea salad (p39) *plus* 1 pear	Tofu stir-fry (p65)	2 large kiwifruit
saturday	Strawberry hotcakes with blueberry sauce (p29)	½ cup baked beans with 2 slices toasted wholegrain bread *plus* 1 apple	Grilled lean beef steak 1 jacket potato with a green salad *plus* 1 multigrain roll *plus* a small tub low-fat natural yogurt	1 apple, fresh, baked or stewed
sunday	Breakfast with the lot (p22) *plus* 1 small tub low-fat fruit yogurt	Niçoise salad (p40) *plus* 1 orange *plus* 1 multigrain roll	Pork loin with couscous and apples (p62) *plus* steamed baby potatoes and green beans	2 scoops low-fat ice-cream (any flavour) with ½ cup raspberries or blueberries

breakfasts

corn fritters with roasted tomato chilli jam

preparation time 20 minutes
cooking time 1 hour 25 minutes
serves 4
per serving 1250kJ (299 cal); 5g total fat (1.2g saturated fat); 48.4g carbohydrate; 8.9g fibre; medium GI

You need 2 medium corn cobs, each weighing about 250g after being trimmed. Roasted tomato chilli jam is best made a day or two ahead to allow the flavours to develop. You can make double the quantity of jam and keep it, covered, in the refrigerator for up to 4 weeks.

serving suggestion Serve with baby spinach leaves.

1 cup (160g) wholemeal self-raising flour
½ teaspoon bicarbonate of soda
½ teaspoon hot paprika
¾ cup (180ml) no-fat milk
2 eggs, beaten lightly
2 cups (330g) fresh corn kernels
1 small red capsicum (150g), chopped finely
2 green onions, sliced thinly
2 tablespoons finely chopped fresh flat-leaf parsley
roasted tomato chilli jam
2 medium tomatoes (380g)
1 small red onion (100g), chopped finely
1 clove garlic, crushed
2cm piece fresh ginger (10g), grated
¼ cup (60ml) lime juice
2 tablespoons brown sugar
2 fresh small red thai chillies, chopped finely

1 Sift flour, soda and paprika into medium bowl. Make well in centre of flour mixture, gradually whisk in combined milk and eggs until batter is smooth. Stir corn, capsicum, onion and parsley into batter.
2 Pour ¼ cup batter into heated lightly greased large frying pan; using spatula, spread batter to shape into a round. Cook about 2 minutes each side or until fritter is browned lightly and cooked through; remove from pan, cover to keep warm. Repeat with remaining batter.
roasted tomato chilli jam Preheat oven to 220°C/200°C fan-forced. Halve tomatoes; place, cut-side up, on lightly oiled oven tray. Roast, uncovered, 30 minutes; chop tomato coarsely. Combine tomato with remaining ingredients in small saucepan; stir over low heat until sugar dissolves. Bring to a boil; simmer, uncovered, about 40 minutes or until mixture is thickened.

grain	amount	soaking liquid	cooking liquid	cooking time	makes
rolled rice	¾ cup (75g)	1½ cups (375ml)	¾ cup (180ml)	10 minutes	1¾ cups per serving 238kJ (57 cal); 0.5g total fat (0g saturated fat); 14.8g carbohydrate; 0.6g fibre
rolled barley	¾ cup (75g)	1½ cups (375ml)	¾ cup (180ml)	25 minutes	1½ cups per serving 276kJ (66 cal); 0.1g total fat (0.1g saturated fat); 11.5g carbohydrate; 2.1g fibre
rolled oats	¾ cup (60g)	1½ cups (375ml)	½ cup (125ml)	10 minutes	1½ cups per serving 233kJ (56 cal); 1.3g total fat (0.2g saturated fat); 9.3g carbohydrate; 1g fibre
rolled rye	¾ cup (75g)	1½ cups (375ml)	1½ cups (375ml)	50 minutes	1¾ cups per serving 248kJ (59 cal); 0.5g total fat (0.3g saturated fat); 12.1g carbohydrate; 2.3g fibre
rolled triticale	¾ cup (75g)	1½ cups (375ml)	1½ cups (375ml)	45 minutes	1¼ cups per serving 244kJ (58 cal); 0.5g total fat (0g saturated fat); 11.7g carbohydrate; 0.6g fibre

porridge with rolled grains

We used water to make these porridges, but skim milk or various fruit juices are an option, if desired. The amounts given above for each type of porridge are enough to make 4 servings.

1 Place grain and soaking liquid in medium bowl, cover; stand at room temperature overnight.
2 Place undrained grain in medium saucepan; cook, stirring, until mixture comes to a boil. Add cooking liquid; simmer, uncovered, for required cooking time. Serve warm with topping of your choice.

toppings

These toppings are enough for a single serving of porridge.

½ cup (125ml) no-fat milk
189kJ (45 cal); 0.1g total fat (0.1g saturated fat); 6.5g carbohydrate; 0g fibre
1 teaspoon honey
94kJ (23 cal); 0g total fat (0g saturated fat); 22.2g carbohydrate; 0g fibre
1 tablespoon low-fat vanilla yogurt
68kJ (16 cal); 0g total fat (0g saturated fat); 2.4g carbohydrate; 0g fibre
pinch cinnamon 0g total fat; 6kJ (2 cal)
½ mashed banana
240kJ (57 cal); 0.1g total fat (0g saturated fat); 45.8g carbohydrate; 5.1g fibre
1 tablespoon dried fruit
156kJ (37 cal); 0.1g total fat (0.1g saturated fat); 13g carbohydrate; 1.1g fibre
2 teaspoons toasted shredded coconut
79kJ (19 cal); 2g total fat (1.7g saturated fat); 0.2g carbohydrate; 0.4g fibre

rolled barley

rolled rice

rolled rye

rolled oats

rolled triticale

rice porridge with raisins

preparation time 10 minutes
cooking time 30 minutes **serves** 4
per serving 789kJ (188 cal);
0.4g total fat (0.2g saturated fat);
0.7g fibre; 38.6g carbohydrate; low GI

Doongara rice, also labelled "Clever Rice", can be found at your local supermarket.

½ cup (100g) doongara rice
½ cup (125ml) water
2 cups (500ml) no-fat milk
1 tablespoon brown sugar
¼ cup (40g) raisins
pinch nutmeg
⅔ cup (160ml) no-fat milk, warmed, extra

1 Combine rice and the water in small saucepan; bring to a boil. Simmer, uncovered, until liquid is absorbed.
2 Add milk, sugar and raisins; simmer about 20 minutes or until rice is tender, stirring occasionally. Stir in nutmeg; serve warm with extra milk.

date and bran muffins

preparation time 15 minutes
(plus standing time)
cooking time 25 minutes
makes 12 muffins
per muffin 739kJ (177cal);
4.1g total fat (0.8g saturated fat);
30.6g carbohydrate; 5.7g fibre; high GI

1½ cups (100g) unprocessed bran
1½ cups (375ml) no-fat milk
1¼ cups (185g) self-raising flour
½ cup (100g) firmly packed brown sugar
2 teaspoons ground cinnamon
⅓ cup (90g) low-fat dairy-free spread, melted
1 egg
1 cup (160g) finely chopped seeded dried dates

1 Preheat oven to 180°C/160°C fan-forced. Grease 12-hole ⅓ cup (80ml) muffin pan.
2 Combine bran and milk in large bowl; stand 5 minutes.
3 Stir flour, sugar and cinnamon into bran mixture until combined. Add remaining ingredients; stir, but do not overmix. Divide muffin mixture among pan holes.
4 Bake about 25 minutes. Turn muffins onto wire rack to cool.

buckwheat pancakes with lemon cream

preparation time 10 minutes
cooking time 10 minutes **serves** 4
per serving 837kJ (200 cal); 6g total fat
(3.3g saturated fat); 28.5g carbohydrate;
3.2g fibre; medium GI

½ cup (75g) buckwheat flour
¼ cup (35g) wholemeal
  self-raising flour
1½ teaspoons baking powder
½ teaspoon ground cinnamon
2 egg whites
¾ cup (180ml) no-fat milk
1 tablespoon lemon juice
2 tablespoons maple syrup
20g low-fat dairy-free spread, melted
2 teaspoons coarsely grated
  lemon rind
lemon cream
⅓ cup (80g) light sour cream
1 teaspoon finely grated
  lemon rind
1 teaspoon caster sugar

1 Sift flours, baking powder and cinnamon into medium bowl; gradually whisk in combined egg white, milk, juice and syrup. Stir spread into batter.

2 Pour ¼ cup batter into heated lightly greased small frying pan; cook about 2 minutes or until bubbles appear on the surface. Turn pancake; cook until browned lightly on other side. Remove from pan; cover to keep warm. Repeat with remaining batter. Serve with lemon cream; top with rind.

lemon cream Place ingredients in small bowl; stir until combined.

citrus compote

strawberry smoothie

mocha smoothie

peach smoothie

citrus compote

preparation time 20 minutes **serves** 4
per serving 685kJ (164 cal);
0.7g total fat (0g saturated fat);
33.3g carbohydrate; 6.7g fibre; low GI

Pink or ruby grapefruit have coral-pink flesh and a shell-pink blush to their skin. They are sweeter than the yellow-skinned variety.

2 large limes (160g)
3 large oranges (900g)
2 medium pink grapefruit (850g)
2 teaspoons white sugar
½ vanilla bean, split
1 tablespoon small fresh mint leaves

1 Grate the rind of 1 lime and 1 orange finely; reserve grated rind. Peel remaining lime, remaining oranges and grapefruit.
2 Segment all citrus over a large bowl to save juice, removing and discarding membrane from each segment. Add segments to bowl with sugar, vanilla bean and reserved rind; stir gently to combine.
3 Stand, covered, at room temperature 5 minutes; sprinkle with mint leaves.

strawberry smoothie

preparation time 10 minutes **serves** 4
per serving 783kJ (187 cal);
3.5g total fat (2.3g saturated fat);
27g carbohydrate; 1.4g fibre; low GI

200g low-fat frozen
    strawberry yogurt
250g strawberries
1 litre (4 cups) no-fat milk

1 Soften yogurt slightly; cut into pieces. Hull strawberries; cut each in half.
2 Blend or process ingredients, in batches, until smooth.

mocha smoothie

preparation time 5 minutes **serves** 4
per serving 896kJ (214 cal); 4g total fat (0.9g saturated fat); 19.3g carbohydrate; 0.2g fibre; low GI

1 litre (4 cups) no-fat milk
1 cup (250ml) low-fat
    chocolate mousse
1 cup (250ml) low-fat
    chocolate ice-cream
1 tablespoon instant coffee granules
½ teaspoon vanilla essence

1 Blend or process ingredients, in batches, until smooth.

peach smoothie

preparation time 10 minutes **serves** 4
per serving 638kJ (152 cal);
0.9g total fat (0.1g saturated fat);
29g carbohydrate; 3.7g fibre; low GI

2 cups (500ml) no-fat soy milk
2 medium bananas (400g),
    chopped coarsely
4 medium peaches (600g),
    chopped coarsely
½ teaspoon ground cinnamon

1 Blend or process ingredients, in batches, until smooth.

breakfast with the lot

preparation time 10 minutes
cooking time 25 minutes **serves** 4
per serving 680kJ (160 cal); 7g total fat
(2g saturated fat); 12g carbohydrate;
2.1g fibre; medium GI

2 large egg tomatoes (180g),
    quartered
4 eggs
4 slices multigrain bread, toasted
60g light ham
50g baby spinach leaves

1 Preheat oven to 220°C/200°C fan-forced. Line oven tray with baking paper.

2 Place tomato, cut-side up, on tray; roast, uncovered, about 25 minutes or until softened and browned lightly.

3 Meanwhile, place enough water in a large shallow frying pan to come halfway up the side; bring to a boil. Break eggs, one at a time, into small bowl, sliding each into pan; allow water to return to a boil. Cover pan, turn off heat; stand about 4 minutes or until a light film of egg white has set over each yolk.

4 Using an egg slide, remove eggs, one at a time, from pan; place egg, still on slide, on absorbent-paper-lined saucer to blot up any poaching liquid. Serve toast topped with ham, spinach, egg then tomato.

egg tomatoes, also known as roma or plum tomatoes, are small and oval in shape; they are often used in Italian dishes.

morning trifles

preparation time 20 minutes **serves** 4
per serving 527kJ (126 cal);
0.7g total fat (0.1g saturated fat);
20.4g carbohydrate; 6.4g fibre; low GI

You need 5 passionfruit for this recipe.

⅓ cup (20g) All-Bran
⅓ cup (20g) Special K
⅓ cup (20g) puffed wheat
250g strawberries, hulled
1 cup (280g) low-fat vanilla yogurt
⅓ cup (80ml) passionfruit pulp

1 Combine cereals in small bowl.
2 Cut six strawberries in half; reserve. Slice remaining strawberries thinly.
3 Divide half of the cereal mixture among four 1-cup (250ml) serving bowls; divide half of the yogurt, all the strawberry slices and half of the passionfruit pulp among bowls.
4 Continue layering with remaining cereal and yogurt; top with reserved strawberry halves and remaining passionfruit pulp.

untoasted muesli

preparation time 10 minutes **serves** 6
per serving 1132kJ (270 cal);
4.1g total fat (0.7g saturated fat);
47.3g carbohydrate; 6.2g fibre; medium GI

You can use fruit juice, such as apple juice, instead of the milk, if you prefer.

2 cups (180g) rolled oats
½ cup (35g) All-Bran
1 tablespoon sunflower seed kernels
⅓ cup (55g) sultanas
¼ cup (35g) finely chopped
   dried apricots
½ cup (80g) finely chopped
   seeded dried dates
3 cups (750ml) no-fat milk
½ cup (140g) low-fat yogurt

1 Combine rolled oats, All-Bran, kernels and dried fruit in large bowl.
2 Divide muesli and milk among serving bowls; top with yogurt.

egg-white omelette

preparation time 10 minutes
cooking time 15 minutes **serves** 4
per serving 1268kJ (303 cal);
6.3g total fat (1.7g saturated fat);
33.1g carbohydrate; 7.4g fibre; low GI

150g light ham
200g button mushrooms,
    sliced thinly
12 egg whites
¼ cup finely chopped fresh chives
2 medium tomatoes (380g),
    chopped coarsely
½ cup (45g) coarsely grated
    low-fat cheddar
8 slices wholemeal bread, toasted

1 Cut ham into thin strips; cook in heated large frying pan, stirring, until browned lightly. Remove from pan. Cook mushrooms in same pan, stirring, until browned lightly.
2 Using electric mixer, beat three of the egg whites in small bowl until soft peaks form; fold in a quarter of the chives.
3 Preheat grill.
4 Pour egg-white mixture into heated lightly oiled 20cm frying pan; cook, uncovered, over low heat until just browned underneath.
5 Place pan under grill; cook until top just sets.
6 Place a quarter of the tomato on one half of the omelette, return to grill; cook until tomato is hot and top is browned lightly. Gently place a quarter each of the cheese, ham and mushroom over tomato; fold over to enclose filling. Carefully transfer omelette to serving plate; cover to keep warm.
7 Repeat with remaining egg whites, chives and fillings.
8 Serve omelettes with toast.

button mushrooms have a mild earthy flavour and can be eaten raw or cooked.

strawberry hotcakes with blueberry sauce

preparation time 15 minutes
cooking time 20 minutes **serves** 6
per serving 1208kJ (296 cal);
2.1g total fat (0.5g saturated fat);
48.8g carbohydrate; 6.9g fibre; low GI

1 egg, separated
2 egg whites, extra
½ cup (125ml) apple sauce
1 teaspoon vanilla essence
2 cups (560g) low-fat yogurt
1¾ cups (280g) wholemeal
   self-raising flour
250g strawberries, hulled,
   chopped coarsely
blueberry sauce
150g blueberries, chopped coarsely
2 tablespoons white sugar
1 tablespoon water

1 Using electric mixer, beat all egg whites in small bowl until soft peaks form.
2 Combine egg yolk, apple sauce, essence, yogurt, flour and strawberries in large bowl; fold in egg whites.
3 Pour 2 tablespoons batter into heated lightly greased large frying pan; using spatula, spread batter into a round. Cook, over low heat, about 2 minutes or until bubbles appear on the surface. Turn hotcake; cook until browned lightly on other side. Remove from pan; cover to keep warm. Repeat with remaining batter. Serve with blueberry sauce.
blueberry sauce Combine ingredients in small saucepan; bring to a boil, stirring constantly. Simmer 2 minutes. Remove from heat; cool. Blend or process blueberry mixture until smooth.

blueberries, with a juicy centre and sweet taste, have easily become one of our year-round all-time-favourite berries.

snacks & light meals

kumara and coriander soup

preparation time 10 minutes
cooking time 35 minutes **serves** 4
per serving 880kJ (210 cal);
2.9g total fat (0.7g saturated fat);
34.6g carbohydrate; 6.8g fibre; low GI

1 teaspoon canola oil
2 medium leeks (700g),
  chopped coarsely
3 cloves garlic, quartered
2 medium kumara (800g),
  chopped coarsely
1 litre (4 cups) chicken stock
⅔ cup (160ml) light evaporated milk
⅓ cup finely chopped
  fresh coriander

1 Heat oil in large saucepan; cook leek and garlic, stirring, until leek softens. Add kumara; cook, stirring, 5 minutes. Add stock; bring to a boil. Simmer, covered, about 20 minutes or until kumara softens.

2 Blend or process soup, in batches, until smooth; return soup to same cleaned pan. Simmer, uncovered, until soup thickens slightly.

3 Add evaporated milk and coriander; stir over heat, without boiling, until heated through. Top with fresh coriander leaves, if desired.

tofu cakes with sweet chilli dipping sauce

preparation time 15 minutes (plus standing time)
cooking time 15 minutes
makes 20 tofu cakes
per cake 326kJ (78 cal); 1.7g total fat (0.3g saturated fat); 12.9g carbohydrate; 0.8g fibre; medium GI

You need to cook ⅓ cup basmati rice for this recipe.

300g fresh firm tofu
1 cup (150g) cooked basmati rice
3 teaspoons red curry paste
2 green onions, chopped finely
1 tablespoon coarsely chopped fresh coriander
1 egg, beaten lightly

sweet chilli dipping sauce
¼ cup (60ml) white vinegar
½ cup (110g) caster sugar
½ teaspoon salt
¾ cup (180ml) water
½ small red onion (50g), chopped finely
½ small carrot (35g), chopped finely
½ lebanese cucumber (65g), seeded, chopped finely
2 tablespoons coarsely chopped fresh coriander
⅓ cup (80ml) sweet chilli sauce

1 Press tofu between two chopping boards with a weight on top, raise one end slightly to allow tofu liquid to drain away. Stand 20 minutes; chop coarsely. Blend or process tofu until smooth.

2 Preheat oven 200°C/180°C fan-forced. Line oven tray with baking paper.

3 Combine tofu in medium bowl with rice, paste, onion, coriander and egg.

4 Shape level tablespoons of tofu mixture into rounds; place on oven tray. Bake, uncovered, about 10 minutes or until browned lightly and heated through. Serve tofu cakes with sweet chilli dipping sauce.

sweet chilli dipping sauce Place vinegar, sugar, salt and the water in small saucepan; bring to a boil. Boil, stirring, about 2 minutes or until sugar dissolves. Pour vinegar mixture over remaining ingredients in medium heatproof bowl; stir to combine.

oven-roasted potato wedges with tomato relish

preparation time 15 minutes
cooking time 40 minutes **serves** 6
per serving 954kJ (228 cal);
1.2g total fat (0.1g saturated fat);
29.5g carbohydrate; 4.5g fibre; high GI

1kg large new potatoes
vegetable-oil spray
1 teaspoon salt
1 teaspoon freshly ground
    black pepper
4 medium tomatoes (760g),
    chopped finely
1 small brown onion (80g),
    chopped finely
2 tablespoons brown sugar
2 tablespoons red wine vinegar
1 teaspoon mustard powder

1 Preheat oven to 240°C/220°C fan-forced.
2 Halve potatoes lengthways; cut each half into wedges. Place wedges, in single layer, in large shallow baking dish; spray with oil, sprinkle with salt and pepper. Bake, uncovered, about 30 minutes or until browned and crisp, turning occasionally.
3 Meanwhile, place tomato, onion, sugar, vinegar and mustard in medium saucepan; bring to a boil. Simmer, uncovered, about 30 minutes or until relish thickens. Serve potato wedges with relish.

beetroot soup

preparation time 10 minutes
(plus refrigeration time)
cooking time 35 minutes **serves** 4
per serving 519kJ (124 cal); 3.4g total fat
(1.4g saturated fat); 17.2g carbohydrate;
4.7g fibre; medium GI

1 teaspoon olive oil
1 small brown onion (80g),
    chopped coarsely
1 clove garlic, crushed
3 medium beetroot (500g),
    trimmed, chopped coarsely
1 medium apple (150g), cored,
    chopped coarsely
1 litre (4 cups) vegetable stock
½ cup (125ml) water
¼ cup (60ml) lemon juice
¼ teaspoon Tabasco sauce
½ lebanese cucumber (65g),
    seeded, chopped finely
½ small red onion (50g),
    chopped finely
1 tablespoon light sour cream

1 Heat oil in large saucepan; cook onion and garlic, stirring, until onion softens. Add beetroot, apple, stock and the water; bring to a boil. Simmer, covered, about 20 minutes or until beetroot is tender, stirring occasionally.
2 Blend or process soup, in batches, until smooth. Stir in juice and sauce; refrigerate, covered, until cold.
3 Serve chilled soup topped with combined remaining ingredients.

lamb and tabbouleh wrap

preparation time 35 minutes
(plus standing time)
cooking time 10 minutes
makes 8 wraps
per wrap 1304kJ (311 cal);
4.9g total fat (1.4g saturated fat);
48.4g carbohydrate; 7.7g fibre; medium GI

1 cup (250ml) water
½ cup (80g) burghul
300g can chickpeas, rinsed, drained
⅓ cup (95g) low-fat yogurt
1 teaspoon finely grated lemon rind
1 tablespoon lemon juice
3 green onions, sliced thinly
2 medium tomatoes (380g), seeded, chopped finely
1 lebanese cucumber (130g), seeded, chopped finely
1 cup coarsely chopped fresh flat-leaf parsley
½ cup coarsely chopped fresh mint
1 tablespoon lemon juice, extra
250g lean lamb strips
2 tablespoons sumac
8 slices lavash bread

1 Combine the water and burghul in small bowl; stand 30 minutes. Drain; squeeze burghul with hands to remove excess water.
2 Meanwhile, blend or process chickpeas, yogurt, rind and juice until hummus is smooth.
3 Combine burghul in large bowl with onion, tomato, cucumber and herbs; add extra juice, toss gently until tabbouleh is combined.
4 Toss lamb in sumac; cook, in batches, on heated lightly oiled grill plate (or grill or barbecue) until browned and cooked as desired.
5 Just before serving, spread hummus equally over half of each slice of bread, top with equal amounts of lamb and tabbouleh; roll to enclose filling. Cut into pieces to serve, if desired.

sumac, a purple-red astringent spice, can be teamed with almost anything – from fish to meat or sprinkled over vegetables. You can find sumac at supermarkets and Middle Eastern food stores.

rice and chickpea salad

preparation time 15 minutes
(plus refrigeration time)
cooking time 10 minutes **serves** 6
per serving 929kJ (222 cal);
4.3g total fat (0.2g saturated fat);
26.7g carbohydrate; 2.1g fibre; low GI

Also known as garbanzos, hummus or channa, chickpeas are often used in Mediterranean cooking.

1 cup (200g) doongara rice
1¾ cups (430ml) water
300g can chickpeas, rinsed, drained
¼ cup (40g) sultanas
¼ cup (35g) dried apricots, chopped finely
2 green onions, sliced thinly
2 tablespoons roasted pine nuts
balsamic orange dressing
1 teaspoon finely grated orange rind
⅓ cup (80ml) orange juice
1 tablespoon balsamic vinegar
1 clove garlic, crushed
1cm piece fresh ginger (5g), grated

1 Combine rice and the water in medium heavy-based saucepan; bring to a boil. Simmer, covered, about 8 minutes or until rice is tender. Remove from heat; cover, stand 10 minutes. Fluff rice with fork; cool then refrigerate, covered, until cold.
2 Combine rice with remaining ingredients in large bowl; add balsamic orange dressing, toss gently to combine.
balsamic orange dressing Combine ingredients in screw-topped jar; shake well.

curried chicken and zucchini soup

preparation time 10 minutes
cooking time 25 minutes **serves** 4
per serving 1098kJ (262 cal);
6.7g total fat (2.1g saturated fat);
25.7g carbohydrate; 2.7g fibre; medium GI

Doongara, the Aboriginal word for white lightning, is a gluten-free rice that can be found at your local supermarket.

1 tablespoon low-fat dairy-free spread
1 medium brown onion (150g), chopped finely
1 clove garlic, crushed
1 teaspoon curry powder
½ cup (100g) doongara rice
340g chicken breast fillets, sliced thinly
2 cups (500ml) water
1 litre (4 cups) chicken stock
4 medium zucchini (480g), grated coarsely

1 Melt spread in large saucepan; cook onion and garlic, stirring, until onion softens. Add curry powder; cook, stirring, until mixture is fragrant.
2 Add rice and chicken; cook, stirring, 2 minutes. Add the water and stock; bring to a boil. Simmer, covered, 10 minutes. Add zucchini; cook, stirring, about 5 minutes or until chicken is cooked through.

herbed chicken rice paper rolls

preparation time 30 minutes
cooking time 5 minutes **serves** 4
per serving 891kJ (213 cal);
6.5g total fat (1.4g saturated fat);
22.5g carbohydrate; 2.1g fibre; low GI

200g chicken tenderloins
1 tablespoon coarsely chopped
fresh basil
1 tablespoon coarsely chopped
fresh mint
1 tablespoon white wine vinegar
1 medium carrot (120g)
½ medium red capsicum (100g)
½ lebanese cucumber (65g), seeded
16cm-square rice paper sheets
2 tablespoons finely chopped
roasted unsalted peanuts
1 tablespoon lime juice
2 tablespoons soy sauce
½cm piece fresh ginger (2.5g),
grated

1 Combine chicken, basil, mint and vinegar in medium bowl, cover; refrigerate 10 minutes.
2 Meanwhile, cut carrot, capsicum and cucumber into thin strips.
3 Cook chicken on heated lightly oiled grill plate (or grill or barbecue) until browned lightly and cooked through. Stand 5 minutes; slice thinly.
4 To assemble rolls, place 1 sheet of rice paper in medium bowl of warm water until just softened. Lift sheet from water carefully; place, with one point facing you, on board covered with tea towel. Divide chicken, carrot, capsicum and cucumber along centre of sheet; scatter peanuts over filling. Fold top and bottom corners over filling then roll sheet from side to side to enclose filling. Serve rolls with dipping sauce made with combined remaining ingredients.

niçoise salad

preparation time 15 minutes
cooking time 5 minutes **serves** 4
per serving 568kJ (136 cal);
2.3g total fat (0.7g saturated fat);
7.3g carbohydrate; 3.1g fibre; low GI

mesclun is a gourmet salad mix consisting of young lettuce, baby spinach leaves, mizuna and curly endive.

100g green beans, trimmed
2 x 180g cans tuna in
springwater, drained
1 small red onion (100g),
sliced thinly
2 green onions, sliced thinly
250g cherry tomatoes, halved
100g mesclun
2 teaspoons finely grated lemon rind
½ cup (125ml) lemon juice
1 tablespoon wholegrain mustard
2 cloves garlic, crushed
2 teaspoons white sugar

1 Boil, steam or microwave beans until just tender; cool. Cut beans in half.
2 Combine beans with tuna, onions, tomato and mesclun in large bowl.
3 Whisk remaining ingredients in small bowl; add to salad, toss gently to combine.

chilli and lime chicken salad

preparation time 20 minutes
(plus cooling time)
cooking time 10 minutes **serves** 4
per serving 751kJ (179 cal);
 6.7g total fat; 1.8g saturated fat;
7.2g carbohydrate; 4g fibre; medium GI

1 cup (250ml) water
1 cup (250ml) chicken stock
340g chicken breast fillets
1 small carrot (70g), cut into
  matchsticks
1 small red capsicum (150g),
  sliced thinly
½ small wombok (200g),
  shredded finely
2 green onions, chopped finely
¾ cup (60g) bean sprouts
½ cup firmly packed fresh
  coriander leaves
100g watercress, trimmed
chilli lime dressing
¼ cup (60ml) lime juice
2 tablespoons sweet chilli sauce
1 clove garlic, crushed
1 tablespoon oyster sauce
1 teaspoon sesame oil

1 Bring the water and stock to a boil in large saucepan. Reduce heat; add chicken, simmer about 10 minutes or until chicken is cooked through. Cool chicken in cooking liquid before draining. Discard liquid; slice chicken thinly.

2 Place chicken in large bowl with remaining ingredients; add chilli lime dressing, toss to combine.

chilli lime dressing Combine ingredients in screw-topped jar; shake well.

sweet chilli sauce is a delectable, yet low-fat, Thai sauce; it is fantastic in dressings, dips or stir-fries.

swiss brown mushroom and barley soup

preparation time 10 minutes
cooking time 55 minutes **serves** 4
per serving 607kJ (145kJ); 2.7g total fat
(0.7g saturated fat); 21.7g carbohydrate;
6.4g fibre; medium GI

300g swiss brown
  mushrooms, quartered
1 clove garlic, crushed
2 teaspoons soy sauce
2 teaspoons water
1 small brown onion (80g),
  chopped finely
1 litre (4 cups) chicken stock
1 litre (4 cups) water, extra
½ cup (100g) pearl barley
1 untrimmed celery stalk (150g),
  chopped coarsely
2 small carrots (140g),
  chopped coarsely
½ teaspoon freshly ground
  black pepper

1 Place mushrooms, garlic, sauce and the water in heated large frying pan; cook until mushrooms soften.
2 Cook onion in heated lightly oiled large saucepan, stirring, until softened. Add stock and the extra water; bring to a boil. Add barley; simmer, covered, 30 minutes.
3 Add mushroom mixture to pan with remaining ingredients; cook, uncovered, about 20 minutes or until barley and vegetables are tender.

chicken tikka wrap

preparation time 20 minutes
(plus refrigeration time)
cooking time 15 minutes **serves** 4
per serving 1248kJ (298 cal);
6.3g total fat (1.7g saturated fat);
25.3g carbohydrate; 2.9g fibre; medium GI

340g single chicken breast fillets
1 tablespoon tikka masala
  curry paste
2½ cups (700g) low-fat yogurt
2 lebanese cucumbers (260g),
  seeded, chopped finely
⅓ cup coarsely chopped fresh mint
1 small red onion (100g),
  chopped finely
4 large pitta
100g mesclun

1 Cut chicken fillets in half horizontally; combine in large bowl with paste and 2 tablespoons of yogurt. Cover; refrigerate 3 hours or overnight.
2 Cook chicken, in batches, on heated lightly oiled grill plate (or grill or barbecue) until browned and cooked through. Stand 5 minutes; slice thinly.
3 Combine cucumber, mint, onion and remaining yogurt in medium bowl.
4 Just before serving, spread yogurt mixture over pitta; top with equal amounts of mesclun then chicken. Roll to enclose filling.

beef and
bean tacos

preparation time 15 minutes
cooking time 20 minutes **serves** 4
per serving 654kJ (156 cal);
4.6g total fat (1g saturated fat);
18.4g carbohydrate; 6.8g fibre; medium GI

1 clove garlic, crushed
80g lean beef mince
½ teaspoon chilli powder
¼ teaspoon ground cumin
300g can kidney beans,
    rinsed, drained
2 tablespoons tomato paste
½ cup (125ml) water
1 medium tomato (190g),
    chopped coarsely
4 taco shells
¼ small iceberg lettuce,
    shredded finely
salsa cruda
½ lebanese cucumber (65g),
    seeded, chopped finely
½ small red onion (40g),
    chopped finely
1 small tomato (130g), seeded,
    chopped finely
1 teaspoon mild chilli sauce

1 Preheat oven to 180°C/160°C
fan-forced.
2 Heat lightly oiled large frying pan;
cook garlic and beef, stirring, until
beef is browned all over. Add chilli,
cumin, beans, paste, the water and
tomato; cook, covered, over low heat
about 15 minutes or until mixture
thickens slightly.
3 Meanwhile, place taco shells,
upside-down, on oven tray; heat
tacos, in oven, 5 minutes.
4 Just before serving, fill taco shells
with beef mixture and lettuce; top
with salsa cruda.
salsa cruda Combine ingredients
in small bowl.

roasted
ratatouille with
rye toast

preparation time 15 minutes
cooking time 20 minutes **serves** 4
per serving 766kJ (183 cal);
6.2g total fat (0.8g saturated fat);
24.2g carbohydrate; 8.1g fibre; high GI

4 baby eggplants (240g),
    chopped coarsely
3 small zucchini (270g),
    chopped coarsely
100g button mushrooms,
    chopped coarsely
250g cherry tomatoes, halved
1 small leek (200g),
    chopped coarsely
2 cloves garlic, crushed
1 tablespoon olive oil
½ cup coarsely chopped fresh basil
1 tablespoon finely chopped
    fresh oregano
2 tablespoons balsamic vinegar
4 thick slices dark rye bread,
    toasted

1 Preheat oven to 220°C/200°C
fan-forced.
2 Combine eggplant, zucchini,
mushrooms, tomato, leek, garlic
and oil in large shallow baking dish;
roast, uncovered, stirring occasionally,
about 20 minutes or until vegetables
are tender.
3 Stir basil, oregano and vinegar into
ratatouille. Serve warm on toast.

mains

rosemary, brie and sun-dried tomato chicken on corn mash

preparation time 30 minutes
cooking time 15 minutes **serves** 4
per serving 2124kJ (508 cal);
15g total fat (6g saturated fat);
44.5g carbohydrate; 7.5g fibre; high GI

If sun-dried tomatoes are too dry, reconstitute in hot water; drain before mixing with the rosemary.
You can substitute 125g of wilted baby spinach leaves for the corn, if desired.

serving suggestion A crisp mixed-leaf salad dressed with a splash of vinaigrette suits this main course perfectly.

30g sun-dried tomatoes, chopped finely
1 tablespoon finely chopped fresh rosemary
4 single chicken breast fillets (680g)
60g firm brie, quartered
1kg medium new potatoes, quartered
2 cloves garlic, crushed
2 tablespoons no-fat milk
2 tablespoons light sour cream
310g can creamed corn

1 Combine tomato and rosemary in small bowl.
2 Using small sharp knife, slit a pocket in one side of each chicken fillet, taking care not to cut all the way through. Divide tomato mixture and brie among pockets; secure openings with toothpicks.
3 Cook chicken on heated lightly oiled grill plate (or grill or barbecue) until browned and cooked through; cover to keep warm.
4 Meanwhile, boil, steam or microwave potato until tender; drain. Mash potato in large bowl with garlic, milk and sour cream; fold in corn. Serve chicken with mash.

crisp-skinned snapper with stir-fried vegetables and black beans

preparation time 15 minutes
cooking time 10 minutes **serves** 4
per serving 1223kJ (292 cal);
5.3g total fat (1.4g saturated fat);
12.6g carbohydrate; 5.4g fibre; low GI

Broccolini, a cross between broccoli and chinese kale, is milder and sweeter than broccoli. Each long stem is topped by a loose floret that closely resembles broccoli; from floret to stem, broccolini is completely edible. Substitute gai lan (chinese broccoli) for the broccolini in this recipe, if you prefer.

½ teaspoon sea salt
1 teaspoon coarsely ground black pepper
4 x 200g snapper fillets
1 teaspoon sesame oil
1 large brown onion (200g), cut into thin wedges
1 clove garlic, crushed
1cm piece fresh ginger (5g), grated
1 tablespoon salted black beans, rinsed, drained
1 medium green capsicum (200g), chopped coarsely
1 medium red capsicum (200g), chopped coarsely
6 green onions, sliced thickly
100g snow peas
100g broccolini, chopped coarsely
½ cup (125ml) water
¼ cup (60ml) oyster sauce
2 tablespoons lemon juice
500g baby buk choy, chopped coarsely
1 cup (80g) bean sprouts

1 Combine salt and pepper in small bowl; rub into skin side of each fillet. Cook fish, skin-side down, on heated lightly oiled grill plate (or grill or barbecue) until browned and crisp; turn, cook until browned and cooked as desired. Cover to keep warm.
2 Heat oil in wok; stir-fry brown onion, garlic and ginger until onion softens. Add beans; stir-fry 1 minute. Add capsicums, green onion, snow peas and broccolini; stir-fry until vegetables are just tender.
3 Stir in the water, sauce and juice; cook, stirring, until mixture thickens slightly. Add buk choy and sprouts; stir-fry until heated through. Serve fish on vegetables.

serving suggestion Serve steamed doongara rice with this dish; a small bowl of finely chopped red chilli in soy sauce can be passed to add a bit of zip to the fish.

fried rice

preparation time 10 minutes
cooking time 10 minutes **serves** 4
per serving 1527kJ (365 cal);
8.2g total fat 2.4g saturated fat;
19.6g carbohydrate; 4.2g fibre; medium GI

*Also known as "Clever Rice", doongara
rice is a white, long-grain Australian-grown
rice that can be found at your local
supermarket. You need to cook 1½ cups
of rice for this recipe.*
*Cold rice, cooked the day before you
prepare the recipe, is best for this dish;
the individual grains remain separate from
one another and won't get mushy when
reheated in the wok. Spread the cooked
rice on a tray and allow to cool before
covering and refrigerating overnight.*

2 teaspoons peanut oil
1 medium brown onion (150g),
    chopped coarsely
2 cloves garlic, crushed
2cm piece fresh ginger (10g), grated
300g lean pork mince
1 untrimmed celery stalk (150g),
    sliced thickly
1 small red capsicum (150g),
    chopped coarsely
1 large zucchini (150g),
    chopped coarsely
4 cups (600g) cooked doongara rice
¾ cup (90g) frozen peas, thawed
¼ cup (60ml) soy sauce
2 green onions, sliced thinly

1 Heat oil in wok; stir-fry brown
onion, garlic and ginger until onion
has just softened. Add pork; stir-fry
until brown and cooked through.
2 Add celery, capsicum and
zucchini; stir-fry until just tender.
Add rice, peas and sauce; stir-fry
until hot. Toss green onion through
fried rice just before serving.

kecap manis, also spelt ketjap manis, is
an Indonesian thick, sweet soy sauce that
adds a great flavour to stir-fries.
serving suggestion Try topping each
serving with a just-fried egg garnished
with freshly chopped red chilli. Pass the
kecap manis so that everyone can spoon
a little over the egg and rice.

silver beet, mushroom and capsicum frittata

preparation time 15 minutes
cooking time 45 minutes **serves** 4
per serving 809kJ (193 cal);
6.7g total fat (1.6g saturated fat);
19.3g carbohydrate; 8.3g fibre; medium GI

This frittata is just as good eaten at room temperature as it is hot from the oven.

500g silver beet, trimmed,
   chopped coarsely
1 tablespoon low-fat
   dairy-free spread
1 medium brown onion (150g),
   chopped finely
2 cloves garlic, crushed
1 medium red capsicum (200g),
   chopped finely
2 trimmed celery stalks (100g),
   chopped finely
100g button mushrooms,
   sliced thinly
2 large carrots (360g),
   grated coarsely
¼ cup (40g) polenta
¼ cup coarsely chopped fresh basil
3 eggs, beaten lightly
3 egg whites, beaten lightly
⅓ cup (80ml) no-fat milk

1 Preheat oven to 180°C/160°C fan-forced. Line 20cm x 30cm lamington pan with baking paper.
2 Boil, steam or microwave silver beet; drain on absorbent paper.
3 Melt spread in large deep frying pan; cook onion and garlic, stirring, until onion softens. Add capsicum, celery and mushrooms; cook, stirring, until vegetables just soften.
4 Stir silver beet, carrot, polenta and basil into vegetable mixture. Remove from heat; cool 5 minutes.
5 Stir in combined eggs, whites and milk. Spread frittata mixture into pan; bake, uncovered, about 35 minutes or until browned lightly and firm to the touch.

silver beet, also known as swiss chard or chard, is a leafy, dark green vegetable.
serving suggestion Serve frittata with a salad of mixed grape, cherry and teardrop tomatoes.

herb-crusted lamb racks with kipfler potatoes and leek

preparation time 25 minutes
cooking time 55 minutes **serves** 4
per serving 1829kJ (437 cal);
13.7g total fat (5.6g saturated fat);
40.1g carbohydrate; 7.9g fibre; high GI

*Herbed breadcrumb mixture can be
patted onto racks the day before serving.
Cover and refrigerate overnight.*

4 x 3 frenched-trimmed
  lamb cutlet racks (900g)
¼ cup (20g) fresh white
  breadcrumbs
1 tablespoon finely chopped
  fresh rosemary
1 tablespoon finely chopped
  fresh flat-leaf parsley
2 teaspoons finely chopped
  fresh thyme
3 cloves garlic, crushed
3 teaspoons bottled
  coriander pesto
1kg kipfler potatoes,
  halved lengthways
vegetable-oil spray
1 teaspoon sea salt
2 medium leeks (700g), trimmed
2 teaspoons low-fat
  dairy-free spread
¼ cup (60ml) chicken stock
¼ cup (60ml) dry white wine

1 Preheat oven to 200°C/180°C
fan-forced.
2 Remove excess fat from lamb.
Combine breadcrumbs, herbs, garlic
and pesto in small bowl. Press
breadcrumb mixture onto lamb racks,
cover; refrigerate until required.
3 Place potato in large shallow baking
dish; spray with oil, sprinkle with salt.
Roast, uncovered, 20 minutes.
4 Place lamb on top of potato; roast,
uncovered, 10 minutes. Reduce
oven temperature to 150°C/130°C
fan-forced; cook further 20 minutes
or until potato is tender and lamb is
cooked as desired.
5 Meanwhile, cut leeks into 10cm
lengths; slice thinly lengthways. Melt
spread in large frying pan; cook leek,
stirring, until leek softens. Stir in stock
and wine; bring to a boil. Simmer,
uncovered, until liquid reduces by half.
6 Stand lamb 5 minutes before
cutting racks into cutlets; serve
cutlets with potato and leek.

serving suggestion Mesclun with a
lemon and rosemary-scented vinaigrette
marries beautifully with this main course.

cajun-spiced fish with roasted corn salsa

preparation time 15 minutes
cooking time 25 minutes **serves** 4
per serving 1832kJ (438 cal);
15g total fat (3.4g saturated fat);
26.1g carbohydrate; 8.7g fibre; low GI

We used blue-eye fillets for this recipe, but you can use whichever firm white fish fillet you prefer.

1 clove garlic, crushed
1 tablespoon low-fat
  dairy-free spread, melted
2 teaspoons sweet paprika
½ teaspoon ground cumin
1 teaspoon ground white pepper
¼ teaspoon cayenne pepper
4 x 200g firm white fish fillets
3 trimmed corn cobs (750g)
1 small red onion (100g),
  chopped coarsely
1 medium avocado (250g),
  chopped coarsely
250g cherry tomatoes, halved
2 tablespoons lime juice
¼ cup coarsely chopped
  fresh coriander

1 Preheat oven to 220°C/200°C fan-forced.
2 Combine garlic and spread in small bowl; combine spices in another small bowl.
3 Place fish on oven tray; brush both sides with garlic mixture, sprinkle with combined spices. Roast, uncovered, about 15 minutes or until browned both sides and cooked as desired.
4 Roast corn on heated lightly oiled grill plate (or grill or barbecue) until browned all over. When corn is cool enough to handle, cut kernels from cobs with small, sharp knife.
5 Combine corn kernels in medium bowl with remaining ingredients. Serve fish with salsa.

serving suggestion A stack of warmed flour tortillas accompanies this flavoursome dish extremely well. Serve the fish and salsa with tortillas warmed briefly in a microwave oven until they become pliable.

artichoke risotto

preparation time 10 minutes
cooking time 25 minutes **serves** 6
per serving 1353kJ (323 cal);
4.5g total fat (1.2g saturated fat);
37g carbohydrate; 1.8g fibre; medium GI

*While the short-grained arborio rice is
traditionally used in a risotto, we chose to
use the longer-grained doongara rice here
because it has both a lower GI rating and
is more amenable to being cooked with
the liquids added all at once.*

2 teaspoons olive oil
1 medium brown onion (150g),
   chopped finely
3 cloves garlic, crushed
6 green onions, sliced thinly
2 cups (400g) doongara rice
¾ cup (180ml) dry white wine
1½ cups (375ml) chicken stock
3 cups (750ml) water
400g can artichoke hearts,
   drained, sliced thinly
½ cup (40g) finely grated parmesan

1 Heat oil in large saucepan; cook
brown onion, garlic and half the
green onion, stirring, until brown onion
softens. Add rice, wine, stock and the
water; bring to a boil. Simmer, covered,
15 minutes, stirring occasionally.
2 Stir in artichokes, cheese and
remaining green onion; cook, stirring,
about 5 minutes or until artichokes
are heated through.

lentil cottage pie

preparation time 10 minutes
cooking time 45 minutes **serves** 4
per serving 1341kJ (320 cal);
7.2g total fat (1.2g saturated fat);
45.1g carbohydrate; 11.3g fibre; high GI

*If you're not concerned with keeping the
fat content of this dish low, you can stir
½ cup finely grated parmesan into the
mash before baking the cottage pie.*

800g medium new potatoes,
   quartered
2 tablespoons low-fat
   dairy-free spread
1 medium brown onion (150g),
   chopped finely
1 clove garlic, crushed
415g can crushed tomatoes
1 cup (250ml) vegetable stock
1 cup (250ml) water
2 tablespoons tomato paste
⅓ cup (80ml) dry red wine
⅔ cup (130g) red lentils
1 medium carrot (120g),
   chopped finely
½ cup (60g) frozen peas, thawed
2 tablespoons worcestershire
   sauce
⅓ cup coarsely chopped fresh
   flat-leaf parsley

1 Boil, steam or microwave potato
until tender; drain. Mash in large
bowl with half the spread.
2 Melt remaining spread in deep
medium frying pan; cook onion and
garlic, stirring, until onion softens.
Add undrained tomatoes, stock,
the water, paste, wine, lentils and
carrot; bring to a boil. Simmer,
uncovered, 15 minutes, stirring
occasionally. Add peas, sauce and
parsley; cook, uncovered, 5 minutes.
3 Preheat oven to 220°C/200°C
fan-forced.
4 Spoon lentil mixture into shallow
1-litre (4 cup) ovenproof dish. Spread
potato mash on top. Bake, uncovered,
20 minutes. Stand pie 10 minutes
before serving.

pork loin with couscous and apples

preparation time 35 minutes
cooking time 1 hour **serves** 4
per serving 2094kJ (501 cal);
11.6g total fat (3.5g saturated fat);
54.4g carbohydrate; 3g fibre; low GI

We used Granny Smith apples in this recipe. To simplify this recipe, ask your butcher to remove any excess fat and butterfly the pork for you.

⅔ cup (130g) couscous
⅔ cup (160ml) boiling water
2 tablespoons finely chopped
    seeded prunes
2 teaspoons roasted pine nuts
2 tablespoons coarsely chopped
    fresh coriander
2 tablespoons coarsely chopped
    fresh flat-leaf parsley
500g rindless, boneless pork loin
2½ cups (625ml) apple cider
2 medium apples (300g), peeled,
    cored, sliced thickly
1 large red onion (300g), cut into
    thick wedges
2 tablespoons brown sugar

1 Preheat oven to 200°C/180°C fan-forced.
2 Combine couscous with the water in medium heatproof bowl, cover; stand about 5 minutes or until water is absorbed, fluffing with fork occasionally. Toss prunes, nuts, coriander and parsley into couscous.
3 Remove excess fat from pork. Place pork on board, upside-down; slice through thickest part of pork horizontally, without cutting through at the other side. Open pork out to form one large piece; press 1 cup of the couscous mixture against loin along width of pork. Roll pork to enclose stuffing, securing with kitchen string at 2cm intervals.
4 Place rolled pork on rack in large shallow flameproof baking dish; pour 2 cups of cider over pork. Roast, uncovered, about 50 minutes or until cooked through. Remove pork from baking dish; cover to keep warm.
5 Place remaining couscous mixture in small ovenproof dish; cook, covered, about 10 minutes or until heated through.
6 Meanwhile, heat pan juices in baking dish on top of stove; add remaining cider, apple, onion and sugar. Cook, stirring, until apple is just tender. Serve sliced pork with apple mixture and couscous.

serving suggestion A salad made of grated red cabbage, caraway seeds and sliced green onions, dressed in a cider vinaigrette, is the perfect accompaniment for this dish.

tofu stir-fry

preparation time 20 minutes
(plus standing time)
cooking time 35 minutes **serves** 6
per serving 1379kJ (330 cal);
8.7g total fat; (1.3g saturated fat);
42.5g carbohydrate; 4.9g fibre; low GI

*Some Asian supermarkets sell tofu
already fried and cut into squares; while
this will contain more fat than our oven-
browned tofu, it also will shorten the
preparation time for this dish.*

400g fresh firm tofu
400g fresh egg noodles
1 tablespoon sesame oil
2 cloves garlic, crushed
2 fresh small red thai chillies,
    sliced thinly
1 small red onion (100g), cut
    into wedges
1 medium red capsicum (200g),
    chopped coarsely
150g green beans, halved
200g swiss brown
    mushrooms, halved
4 green onions, sliced thinly
2 tablespoons soy sauce
2 tablespoons oyster sauce
1 tablespoon brown sugar

1 Preheat oven to 220°C/200°C
fan-forced. Line oven tray with
baking paper.
2 Press tofu between two chopping
boards, place weight on top; elevate
boards slightly to allow tofu liquid to
drain away. Stand 20 minutes; cut
tofu into 2cm cubes. Place tofu on
oven tray; cook, uncovered, about
25 minutes or until browned lightly.
3 Meanwhile, place noodles in large
heatproof bowl, cover with boiling
water; separate with fork, drain.
Cover to keep warm.
4 Heat oil in wok; stir-fry garlic, chilli
and red onion until onion softens.
Add capsicum; stir-fry 2 minutes.
Add beans and mushrooms; stir-fry
until vegetables are just tender. Add
tofu, green onion, sauces and sugar;
stir-fry until sauce thickens slightly.
Serve stir-fry tossed with noodles.

tofu, also known as bean curd, is the
perfect substitute for meat when making
vegetarian dishes.

tarragon chicken with carrot mash and leek

preparation time 20 minutes (plus refrigeration time)
cooking time 25 minutes **serves** 4
per serving 1296kJ (310 cal); 10.2g total fat (3.5g saturated fat); 9.3g carbohydrate; 5.3g fibre; low GI

You need 12 bamboo skewers for this recipe; soak them in water for at least an hour before using to avoid them splintering or scorching.

Do not puree the carrot mixture too far in advance because it could separate if left to stand too long.

680g single chicken breast fillets, sliced thickly
1 tablespoon finely chopped fresh tarragon
1 tablespoon wholegrain mustard
2 tablespoons low-fat dairy-free spread
2 large leeks (500g), trimmed, chopped finely
4 medium carrots (480g), chopped coarsely
1½ cups (375ml) chicken stock
pinch nutmeg

1 Thread equal amounts of chicken onto each of 12 skewers. Press combined tarragon and mustard all over chicken, cover; refrigerate 30 minutes.

2 Melt spread in large frying pan; cook leek, stirring, until softened. Cover to keep warm.

3 Preheat oven to 200°C/180°C fan-forced.

4 Boil or microwave carrot in stock until just tender; strain over small bowl. Reserve ½ cup of the stock; discard remainder. Blend or process carrot with nutmeg until pureed. Cover to keep warm.

5 Cook chicken and reserved liquid in large shallow baking dish, in oven, uncovered, about 15 minutes or until cooked through.

6 Divide carrot mash among serving plates; top with chicken and leek.

serving suggestion Steamed green beans and a fresh baguette are good accompaniments for this main meal.

beef, red wine and chilli casserole with polenta

preparation time 15 minutes
cooking time 1 hour 45 minutes
serves 4
per serving 2058kJ (492 cal); 14.3g total fat (6.2g saturated fat); 26.7g carbohydrate; 3.7g fibre; low GI

As long as the wine you use is good enough to drink with the meal, any dry red will suffice; however, in keeping with the Italian feel of this recipe, we used a Chianti.

2 teaspoons low-fat dairy-free spread
1.5kg lean beef chuck steak, cut into 3cm pieces
2 cloves garlic, crushed
3 fresh small red thai chillies, sliced thinly
2 teaspoons dijon mustard
1 large brown onion (200g), sliced thickly
2 medium tomatoes (380g), chopped coarsely
410g can tomato puree
¾ cup (180ml) dry red wine
½ cup (125ml) beef stock
1.125 litres (4½ cups) water
1 cup (170g) polenta
¼ cup (20g) finely grated parmesan
2 tablespoons coarsely chopped fresh flat-leaf parsley

1 Melt spread in large saucepan; cook beef, in batches, until browned all over. Cook garlic, chilli, mustard and onion in same pan, stirring, until onion softens. Return beef to pan with tomato; cook, stirring, 2 minutes.

2 Add puree, wine, stock and ½ cup of the water to pan; bring to a boil. Simmer, covered, about 1½ hours or until beef is tender, stirring occasionally.

3 Bring the remaining water to a boil in medium saucepan. Add polenta; cook, stirring, over medium heat about 10 minutes or until thickened. Stir cheese into polenta.

4 Stir parsley into casserole just before serving with polenta.

serving suggestion Serve with baby rocket leaves sprinkled with flaked parmesan and a squeeze of lemon juice, if desired.

risoni marinara

preparation time 15 minutes
cooking time 25 minutes **serves** 6
per serving 1563kJ (374 cal);
3.7g total fat (0.8g saturated fat);
48.7g carbohydrate; 4.6g fibre; low GI

Risoni is a small, rice-sized pasta often used in Italian soups; orzo can be used instead of risoni in this recipe.

12 uncooked large prawns (600g)
12 small mussels (200g)
300g squid hoods
2 teaspoons olive oil
1 large brown onion (200g),
    chopped finely
2 cloves garlic, crushed
1 large red capsicum (350g),
    sliced thinly
375g risoni
1½ cups (375ml) water
1½ cups (375ml) chicken stock
½ cup (125ml) dry white wine
pinch saffron threads
1 cup (125g) frozen peas, thawed
1 large tomato (250g), seeded,
    sliced thinly

1 Shell and devein prawns, leaving tails intact. Scrub mussels; remove beards. Cut squid down centre to open out; score the inside in a diagonal pattern then cut into strips.
2 Heat oil in large saucepan; cook onion, garlic and capsicum, stirring, about 3 minutes or until onion softens. Add risoni; stir to coat in onion mixture.
3 Stir in the water, stock, wine and saffron; bring to a boil. Reduce heat; simmer, uncovered, until liquid is absorbed and risoni is just tender, stirring occasionally.
4 Add prawns, mussels, squid, peas and tomato; cook, covered, until prawns are changed in colour and mussels have opened (discard any that do not).

serving suggestion Salad caprese (basil leaves, bocconcini and sliced tomatoes) goes well with this paella-like one-course meal.

linguine with lamb, asparagus and gremolata

preparation time 20 minutes
cooking time 15 minutes **serves** 6
per serving 1382kJ (330 cal);
6.2g total fat (1g saturated fat);
19.8g carbohydrate; 2.9g fibre; low GI

This recipe is good served warm or at room temperature. If not serving immediately, do not toss the ingredients together or the pasta will absorb the dressing.

375g linguine
375g lamb fillets
500g asparagus, trimmed, chopped coarsely
⅓ cup finely grated lemon rind
4 cloves garlic, crushed
1 cup coarsely chopped fresh flat-leaf parsley
½ cup (125ml) lemon juice
8 green onions, sliced thinly
1 tablespoon olive oil

1 Cook pasta in large saucepan of boiling water until just tender; drain. Place in large bowl; cover to keep warm.
2 Meanwhile, cook lamb on heated lightly oiled grill plate (or grill or barbecue) until browned all over and cooked as desired. Cover; stand 5 minutes, slice thinly.
3 Boil, steam or microwave asparagus until just tender; drain.
4 Combine remaining ingredients in small bowl; pour over pasta. Add lamb and asparagus; toss gently to combine.

oven-steamed ocean trout

preparation time 10 minutes
cooking time 15 minutes **serves** 4
per serving 1751kJ (418 cal);
7.9g total fat (1.8g saturated fat);
39g carbohydrate; 5.8g fibre; high GI

Use tweezers to remove any bones from fish. Rinse and drain capers before using to rid them of excess salt or brine.

serving suggestion Accompany the trout with mixed salad leaves.

4 x 200g ocean trout fillets
2 tablespoons lemon juice
1 tablespoon drained capers, rinsed, chopped coarsely
2 teaspoons coarsely chopped fresh dill
1.2kg large new potatoes, sliced thickly

1 Preheat oven to 200°C/180°C fan-forced.
2 Place each fillet on a square of foil large enough to completely enclose fish; top each fillet with equal amounts of juice, capers and dill. Gather corners of foil squares together above fish, twist to close securely.
3 Place parcels on oven tray; cook about 15 minutes or until fish is cooked as desired.
4 Meanwhile, boil, steam or microwave potato until tender.
5 Remove fish from foil; serve with potato.

dhal with egg and eggplant

preparation time 10 minutes
cooking time 1 hour **serves** 4
per serving 1698kJ (406 cal);
10.9g total fat (2.6g saturated fat);
44.6g carbohydrate; 16.7g fibre; low GI

Spoon a whole egg into each of four serving bowls then spoon dhal over the egg.

2 cups (400g) red lentils
2 teaspoons vegetable oil
1 medium brown onion (150g), chopped finely
1 clove garlic, crushed
2 teaspoons ground cumin
½ teaspoon cumin seeds
1 tablespoon tomato paste
1 litre (4 cups) water
2 cups (500ml) vegetable stock
1 large tomato (250g), chopped coarsely
3 baby eggplants (180g), chopped coarsely
4 hard-boiled eggs

1 Rinse lentils in large colander under cold water until water runs clear.
2 Heat oil in large heavy-based saucepan; cook onion, garlic, ground cumin, seeds and paste, stirring, 5 minutes. Add lentils, the water and stock; bring to a boil. Simmer, uncovered, about 40 minutes or until dhal mixture thickens slightly, stirring occasionally.
3 Add tomato and eggplant; simmer, uncovered, about 20 minutes or until dhal is thickened and eggplant is tender, stirring occasionally. Add eggs; stir gently until eggs are heated through.

serving suggestion Serve with a bowl of steamed basmati rice.
A bowl of cucumber raita, made with low-fat plain yogurt and a hint of cumin, completes this Indian meal.

singapore noodles

preparation time 10 minutes
cooking time 20 minutes **serves** 4
per serving 1545kJ (369 cal);
9.9g total fat (2.1g saturated fat);
52.5g carbohydrate; 6.8g fibre; medium GI

250g rice vermicelli
4 eggs, beaten lightly
2 teaspoons vegetable oil
1 medium brown onion (150g),
    chopped coarsely
2 cloves garlic, crushed
2cm piece fresh ginger (10g), grated
150g baby buk choy,
    chopped coarsely
200g snow peas, halved
1 small red capsicum (150g),
    sliced thickly
2 tablespoons soy sauce
2 tablespoons oyster sauce
2 tablespoons sweet chilli sauce
1 cup loosely packed fresh
    coriander leaves
3 cups (240g) bean sprouts

1 Place noodles in large heatproof bowl, cover with boiling water; stand until just tender, drain. Using scissors, cut noodles into 10cm lengths.
2 Heat lightly oiled wok; add half the egg, swirling wok to form thin omelette. Remove omelette from wok; roll into cigar shape, cut into thin slices. Repeat with remaining egg.
3 Heat oil in wok; stir-fry onion until soft. Add garlic and ginger; stir-fry, 1 minute. Add buk choy, snow peas, capsicum and sauces; stir-fry until vegetables are just tender.
4 Add noodles and egg strips with coriander and sprouts to wok; toss gently to combine.

serving suggestion Pass a platter of cucumber spears, quartered hard-boiled eggs, tomato wedges and sliced pawpaw to make this meal authentically Singaporean.

satay beef and stir-fried vegetables with rice

preparation time 20 minutes
cooking time 20 minutes **serves** 6
per serving 1509kJ (361 cal);
12.6g total fat (3.4g saturated fat);
33.9g carbohydrate; 3.6g fibre; low GI

You can use sliced lamb fillets or sliced chicken thigh fillets instead of the beef, if you prefer.

1 cup (200g) basmati rice
1 teaspoon peanut oil
500g lean beef topside, sliced thinly
1 large brown onion (200g),
    sliced thinly
1 clove garlic, crushed
2cm piece fresh ginger (10g), grated
2 fresh small red thai chillies,
    chopped finely
1 medium red capsicum (200g),
    chopped coarsely
1 medium green capsicum (200g),
    chopped coarsely
100g button mushrooms, halved
225g can bamboo shoots,
    rinsed, drained
1 teaspoon curry powder
2 teaspoons cornflour
½ cup (125ml) chicken stock
¼ cup (65g) light smooth
    peanut butter
2 tablespoons oyster sauce
1 tablespoon coarsely chopped
    unsalted roasted peanuts

1 Cook rice in large saucepan of boiling water, uncovered, until just tender; drain. Cover to keep warm.
2 Meanwhile, heat oil in wok; stir-fry beef, in batches, until browned.
3 Reheat meat juices in wok; stir-fry onion and garlic until onion softens. Add ginger, chilli, capsicums, mushrooms, bamboo shoots and curry powder; stir-fry until vegetables are just tender.
4 Blend cornflour with stock in small jug; add to wok, stir to combine. Return beef to wok with peanut butter and sauce; bring to a boil, stirring, until sauce thickens slightly and beef is cooked as desired. Stir in peanuts; serve with rice.

pork vindaloo

preparation time 15 minutes
(plus refrigeration time)
cooking time 50 minutes **serves** 4
per serving 2140kJ (512 cal);
17g total fat (5g saturated fat);
46.9g carbohydrate; 3.2g fibre; low GI

Vindaloo curry paste can be made up to a week ahead and kept, covered tightly, in the refrigerator. Making this dish a day ahead helps intensify the flavours.

2 large brown onions (400g),
   chopped coarsely
5 cloves garlic, quartered
1 teaspoon ground cardamom
½ teaspoon ground clove
1 teaspoon ground cinnamon
2 teaspoons ground cumin
2 teaspoons ground turmeric
2 teaspoons cracked black pepper
3 fresh small red thai chillies,
   quartered
2 teaspoons black mustard seeds
1 tablespoon grated fresh ginger
⅓ cup (80ml) white vinegar
1kg pork fillet, trimmed
1 tablespoon vegetable oil
1 large brown onion (200g),
   sliced thinly
2 tablespoons tamarind paste
2 large tomatoes (500g),
   chopped coarsely
1½ cups (300g) jasmine rice

1 Blend or process chopped onion, garlic, spices, chilli, seeds, ginger and vinegar to a smooth paste.
2 Trim excess fat from pork; cut into 3cm pieces. Combine pork with a quarter of the curry paste in medium bowl; stir to coat pork all over. Cover; refrigerate 3 hours or overnight. Reserve remaining curry paste.
3 Heat oil in large saucepan; cook sliced onion, stirring, until just soft. Add reserved curry paste; cook, stirring, over low heat 5 minutes. Add pork; cook, stirring, about 5 minutes or until pork changes colour. Stir in tamarind paste and tomato; bring to a boil. Simmer, covered, about 40 minutes or until pork is tender and cooked through.
4 Meanwhile, cook rice in large saucepan of boiling water, uncovered, until just tender; drain.
5 Serve curry on rice.

serving suggestion Serve vindaloo with chopped cucumber and fresh pineapple, if desired.

grilled chicken with barley pilaf

preparation time 10 minutes
cooking time 55 minutes **serves** 4
per serving 1726kJ (412 cal);
11.3g total fat (3.4g saturated fat);
34.2g carbohydrate; 7.7g fibre; low GI

If tomatoes are too large, halve them before roasting.

1 cup (200g) pearl barley
2 cups (500ml) water
2 cups (500ml) chicken stock
250g cherry tomatoes
150g yellow teardrop tomatoes
4 chicken breast fillets (680g)
½ teaspoon coarsely ground
   black pepper
½ cup coarsely chopped fresh basil
2 green onions, sliced thinly
1 tablespoon dijon mustard

1 Preheat oven to 240°C/220°C fan-forced.
2 Cook barley with the water and stock in medium saucepan, uncovered, over low heat, about 50 minutes or until most of the liquid is absorbed, stirring occasionally.
3 Meanwhile, place tomatoes on baking-paper-lined oven tray; roast, uncovered, in oven, about 20 minutes or until just browned and softened.
4 Cook chicken on heated lightly oiled grill plate (or grill or barbecue) until browned and cooked through.
5 Stir tomatoes, pepper, basil and onion gently into barley.
6 Dollop chicken with mustard, serve with barley pilaf.

baby spinach leaves drizzled with lemon juice goes well with this dish.

roast baby vegetable pizza

preparation time 15 minutes
cooking time 40 minutes **serves** 4
per serving 1016kJ (243 cal);
2.9g total fat (0.8g saturated fat);
24.2g carbohydrate; 8.1g fibre; high GI

3 small zucchini (160g), sliced thinly
4 baby eggplants (240g), sliced thinly
10 cherry tomatoes, halved
1 baby fennel bulb (130g),
    sliced thinly
100g button mushrooms,
    sliced thinly
⅔ cup (190g) bottled tomato
    pasta sauce
¼ cup coarsely chopped fresh basil
4 wholemeal pocket pitta
⅓ cup (40g) coarsely grated
    low-fat cheddar

1 Preheat oven to 240°C/220°C fan-forced.
2 Place zucchini, eggplant and tomato in lightly oiled shallow medium baking dish; roast, uncovered, 20 minutes.
3 Add fennel, mushrooms and all but 2 tablespoons of the pasta sauce to dish; roast, covered, 10 minutes. Stir basil into vegetable mixture.
4 Divide reserved pasta sauce among bread pieces; top each with equal amounts of the vegetable mixture and cheese. Place on oven tray; cook, uncovered, about 10 minutes or until cheese melts and pizzas are heated through.

thai lamb salad

preparation time 20 minutes
cooking time 10 minutes **serves** 4
per serving 997kJ (238 cal);
4.9g total fat (2g saturated fat);
18.3g carbohydrate; 5.9g fibre; low GI

100g bean thread noodles
500g lamb fillets, trimmed
1 medium red onion (170g),
    sliced thinly
3 green onions, sliced thinly
1 cup (80g) bean sprouts
1 cup loosely packed fresh
    coriander leaves
1 cup loosely packed fresh
    mint leaves
1 cup loosely packed fresh
    vietnamese mint leaves
1 lebanese cucumber (130g),
    seeded, sliced thinly
2 fresh small red thai chillies,
    sliced thinly
200g cherry tomatoes, halved
2 cloves garlic, crushed
1 tablespoon finely chopped
    fresh lemon grass
⅓ cup (80ml) lime juice
1 tablespoon fish sauce
1 tablespoon soy sauce

1 Place noodles in medium heatproof bowl; cover with boiling water. Stand until just tender; drain. Rinse noodles under cold water; drain well.
2 Cook lamb on heated lightly oiled grill plate (or grill or barbecue) until browned and cooked as desired. Stand 5 minutes; slice thinly.
3 Meanwhile, combine onions, sprouts, herbs, cucumber, chilli and tomato in large bowl. Add lamb and combined remaining ingredients; toss to combine. Serve salad with noodles.

desserts

tiramisu

preparation time 20 minutes
cooking time 25 minutes
(plus refrigeration time)
serves 12
per serving 791kJ (189 cal);
4.1g total fat (2g saturated fat);
28g carbohydrate; 0.9g fibre; medium GI

low-fat ricotta turns this wicked dessert into a deliciously light treat that can be enjoyed by all.

3 eggs
½ cup (110g) caster sugar
¼ cup (40g) wholemeal
   self-raising flour
¼ cup (35g) white self-raising flour
¼ cup (35g) cornflour
1 teaspoon gelatine
1 tablespoon cold water
1½ cups (300g) low-fat ricotta
¼ cup (60ml) no-fat milk
¼ cup (55g) caster sugar, extra
2 tablespoons instant coffee granules
2 tablespoons boiling water
⅓ cup (80ml) no-fat milk, extra
½ cup (125ml) coffee-flavoured
   liqueur
10g dark chocolate, grated finely

1 Preheat oven to 180°C/160°C fan-forced. Grease 22cm springform tin; line base with baking paper.
2 Using electric mixer, beat eggs in small bowl until thick and creamy. Gradually add sugar, beating until sugar dissolves. Fold triple-sifted flours into egg mixture until just combined. Spread into tin.
3 Bake, uncovered, about 25 minutes. Turn onto wire rack to cool.
4 Meanwhile, sprinkle gelatine over the cold water in small heatproof jug; place jug in small pan of simmering water, stir until gelatine dissolves. Cool, 5 minutes.
5 Blend or process ricotta, milk and extra sugar until smooth. With motor operating, add gelatine mixture; process until combined.
6 Dissolve coffee in the boiling water in small bowl; add extra milk and liqueur.
7 Cut cake in half horizontally. Return one cake half to same springform tin; brush half the coffee mixture over cake, top with half the ricotta mixture. Repeat with remaining cake half, coffee mixture and ricotta mixture.
8 Refrigerate tiramisu, covered, for at least 3 hours. Sprinkle top with grated chocolate just before serving.

citrus rice pudding

preparation time 15 minutes
cooking time 1 hour 10 minutes
serves 8
per serving 1094kJ (261 cal);
4.8g total fat (1.7g saturated fat);
31.7g carbohydrate; 0.2g fibre; medium GI

Also labelled "Clever Rice", doongara rice is a white long-grain rice grown in Australia that can be found at your local supermarket. You need to cook about ½ cup of rice for this recipe.

2 cups (500ml) no-fat milk
1 vanilla bean, halved lengthways
1 teaspoon finely grated lemon rind
1 teaspoon finely grated lime rind
2 teaspoons finely grated orange rind
2 eggs
1 egg white
½ cup (110g) caster sugar
1½ cups (225g) cooked
   doongara rice
½ cup (125ml) low-fat cream

1 Preheat oven to 160°C/140°C fan-forced. Grease shallow oval 1.5-litre (6 cup) ovenproof dish.
2 Combine milk, vanilla bean and rinds in medium saucepan; bring to a boil. Remove from heat; stand, covered, 5 minutes.
3 Meanwhile, whisk eggs, egg white and sugar in medium bowl. Gradually whisk hot milk mixture into egg mixture; discard vanilla bean.
4 Spread rice into dish; pour egg mixture carefully over rice. Place dish in large baking dish; add enough boiling water to baking dish to come halfway up side of pudding dish.
5 Bake, uncovered, about 1 hour or until set. Serve warm with cream.

vanilla beans contain myriad tiny black seeds that impart their full flavour to both sweet and savoury dishes.

florentines with berry ice-cream

preparation time 10 minutes
cooking time 10 minutes **serves** 8
per serving 599kJ (143 cal);
3.4g total fat (1.4g saturated fat);
25.2g carbohydrate; 0.7g fibre; medium GI

¼ cup (30g) toasted muesli
¼ cup (15g) bran flakes
¼ cup (40g) sultanas,
  chopped coarsely
2 tablespoons finely chopped
  dried apricots
1 tablespoon finely chopped
  glacé cherries
1½ tablespoons flaked
  almonds, toasted
¼ cup (60ml) light condensed milk
1 tablespoon golden syrup
400g low-fat berry ice-cream

1 Preheat oven to 180°C/160°C fan-forced. Grease two oven trays; line each with baking paper.
2 Combine all ingredients except ice-cream in medium bowl.
3 Drop tablespoons of the mixture onto oven trays about 8cm apart, spread into rounds.
4 Bake about 10 minutes or until florentines are browned lightly; cool on trays. Serve 1½ florentines with 2 scoops of ice-cream.

pear oatmeal cake

preparation time 15 minutes
(plus standing time)
cooking time 1 hour **serves** 16
per serving 720kJ (170 cal);
4.5g total fat (0.8g saturated fat);
30g carbohydrate; 2.6g fibre; medium GI

2 x 425g cans pear halves in syrup
1 cup (90g) rolled oats
½ cup (125g) low-fat
  dairy-free spread
½ teaspoon vanilla essence
¾ cup (150g) firmly packed
  brown sugar
2 eggs
¾ cup (110g) white self-raising flour
¾ cup (120g) wholemeal
  self-raising flour
½ teaspoon bicarbonate of soda
2 teaspoons ground ginger

1 Preheat oven to 200°C/180°C fan-forced. Grease deep 23cm-square cake pan; line base and sides with baking paper.
2 Drain pears over small saucepan. Heat syrup with oats, remove from heat; stand 20 minutes.
3 Meanwhile, using electric mixer, beat spread, essence and sugar in small bowl until combined. Beat in eggs, one at a time, until combined.
4 Add oat mixture and combined sifted remaining ingredients; stir until well combined. Pour mixture into pan; place pears on top, cut-side down.
5 Bake, uncovered, about 55 minutes. Serve cake warm.

pink grapefruit granita with hazelnut wafers

preparation time 20 minutes
(plus freezing time)
cooking time 10 minutes **serves** 8
per serving 713kJ (170 cal);
2.3g total fat (0.2g saturated fat);
36.7g carbohydrate; 0.2g fibre; medium GI

*You will need two large pink grapefruit
for this recipe.*

1 cup (250ml) water
1 cup (220g) sugar
1 cup (250ml) fresh
   pink grapefruit juice
¼ cup (60ml) lemon juice
2 egg whites

hazelnut wafers

1 egg white
¼ cup (55g) caster sugar
2 tablespoons hazelnut meal
20g low-fat dairy-free spread, melted

1 Stir the water and sugar in small saucepan over heat, without boiling, until sugar dissolves. Bring to a boil; boil 5 minutes without stirring. Remove from heat; stir in juices, cool.

2 Using electric mixer, beat egg whites in small bowl until soft peaks form. Fold grapefruit syrup into egg white mixture; pour into 10cm x 24cm loaf pan. Cover; freeze 3 hours or overnight.

3 Blend or process granita until pale and creamy. Return to loaf pan, cover; freeze 3 hours or overnight. Serve granita with hazelnut wafers.

hazelnut wafers Preheat oven to 180°C/160°C fan-forced. Grease two oven trays; line with baking paper. Using electric mixer, beat egg white in small bowl until soft peaks form; gradually add sugar, beating until sugar dissolves between additions. Add hazelnut meal and spread; stir until combined. Trace 16 x 7cm circles, 2cm apart, on lined trays. Spread a teaspoon of mixture in each circle. Bake about 5 minutes or until browned lightly. Cool wafers on trays before carefully peeling away paper.

pears poached in cranberry syrup

preparation time 5 minutes
cooking time 45 minutes **serves** 4
per serving 1178kJ (281 cal);
0.2g total fat (0g saturated fat);
26.5g carbohydrate; 3.5g fibre; low GI

*Pears can be poached a day ahead;
reduce the syrup just before serving.
If beurre bosc pears are unavailable,
use packham or williams pears.*

3 cups (750ml) cranberry juice
⅔ cup (160ml) dry white wine
2 cardamom pods, bruised
½ vanilla bean, halved lengthways
4 medium beurre bosc pears (920g)

1 Combine juice, wine, cardamom and vanilla bean in large saucepan.
2 Add peeled pears to pan; bring to a boil. Simmer, covered, about 25 minutes or until tender. Cool pears in syrup.
3 Remove pears from syrup; strain syrup into medium heatproof bowl. Return 2 cups of the strained syrup to same pan (discard remaining syrup); bring to a boil. Boil, uncovered, about 15 minutes or until syrup is reduced by half. Serve pears, hot or cold, with syrup.

apricot strudel

preparation time 20 minutes
cooking time 20 minutes **serves** 6
per serving 585kJ (143 cal);
2.6g total fat (0.2g saturated fat);
20.6g carbohydrate; 2g fibre; medium GI

825g can apricot slices in
  natural syrup, drained
2 tablespoons brown sugar
1 teaspoon ground cinnamon
¾ cup (120g) sultanas
¼ cup (35g) roasted hazelnuts,
  chopped finely
6 sheets fillo pastry
1 tablespoon no-fat milk
1 tablespoon icing sugar

1 Preheat oven to 200°C/180°C fan-forced. Grease oven tray.
2 Combine apricots, sugar, cinnamon, sultanas and nuts in medium bowl.
3 Stack pastry sheets, brushing each lightly with milk as you layer.
4 Spread apricot filling over pastry, leaving 5cm space at edge of both short sides and 2cm at edge of one long side. Fold short sides over; starting from filled long-side edge, roll strudel to enclose filling. Place seam-side down on tray.
5 Brush strudel with remaining milk. Bake, uncovered, about 25 minutes or until browned lightly. Dust strudel with icing sugar before serving, warm or cold, with ice-cream, if desired.

apple bread pudding

preparation time 20 minutes
cooking time 1 hour 10 minutes
serves 6
per serving 698kJ (167 cal);
3.6g total fat (1.1g saturated fat);
25.5g carbohydrate; 1.7g fibre; low GI

2 medium apples (300g)
2 tablespoons brown sugar
1 tablespoon water
2½ cups (625ml) no-fat milk
1 vanilla bean, halved lengthways
4 slices thick fruit bread
3 eggs
½ teaspoon ground cinnamon
¼ teaspoon ground nutmeg

1 Peel, core and quarter apples; cut each quarter into 3mm slices.

2 Dissolve brown sugar in the water in medium frying pan over low heat, add apples; simmer, uncovered, about 5 minutes or until tender, stirring occasionally.

3 Preheat oven to 160°C/140°C fan-forced. Grease deep 1.5-litre (6 cup) ovenproof dish.

4 Combine milk and vanilla bean in medium saucepan; bring to a boil. Remove from heat; stand, covered, 5 minutes. Discard vanilla bean.

5 Meanwhile, cut bread slices into quarters. Arrange bread and apple in alternate layers in dish.

6 Whisk eggs, cinnamon and nutmeg in medium bowl. Gradually whisk hot milk mixture into egg mixture. Pour egg mixture carefully over bread and apple. Place dish in large baking dish; add enough boiling water to baking dish to come halfway up side of pudding dish.

7 Bake, uncovered, about 1 hour or until set. Serve with low-fat ice-cream or cream, if desired.

strawberry and rhubarb muffins

preparation time 15 minutes
cooking time 20 minutes **makes** 12
per muffin 844kJ (202 cal);
4.3g total fat (0.8g saturated fat);
34.2g carbohydrate; 5.2g fibre; medium GI

You need 4 large trimmed rhubarb
stalks for this recipe.

125g strawberries, sliced thinly
3 cups (450g) wholemeal
  self-raising flour
½ cup (100g) firmly packed
  brown sugar
1 teaspoon ground cinnamon
1 teaspoon vanilla essence
60g low-fat dairy-free spread, melted
¾ cup (180ml) no-fat soy milk
2 eggs, beaten lightly
2 cups (250g) finely chopped rhubarb
¼ cup (60g) apple sauce

1 Preheat oven to 200°C/180°C
fan-forced. Grease 12-hole ⅓ cup
(80ml) muffin pan. Reserve 12 slices
of strawberry.
2 Combine flour, sugar and cinnamon
in large bowl. Add essence, spread,
milk and eggs; mix to combine then
gently stir in remaining strawberries,
rhubarb and apple sauce.
3 Divide mixture among pan holes;
top each with a reserved strawberry
slice. Bake about 20 minutes. Serve
warm or at room temperature.

berry mousse

preparation time 10 minutes
(plus refrigeration time) **serves** 4
per serving 708kJ (169 cal);
0.2g total fat (0.1g saturated fat);
32.8g carbohydrate; 0.9g fibre; low GI

2 teaspoons gelatine
2 tablespoons water
2 egg whites
⅓ cup (75g) caster sugar
2 x 200g cartons low-fat
  berry-flavoured yogurt
150g fresh mixed berries

1 Sprinkle gelatine over the water
in small heatproof jug; place jug in
small pan of simmering water, stir
until gelatine dissolves, cool.
2 Meanwhile, using electric mixer,
beat egg whites in small bowl until
soft peaks form. Gradually add
sugar, beating until sugar dissolves.
3 Place yogurt in medium bowl;
stir in gelatine mixture, fold in
egg-white mixture.
4 Spoon mousse mixture into
serving bowl, cover; refrigerate
about 2 hours or until set. Top
mousse with berries to serve.

plum and cinnamon cake

preparation time 15 minutes
cooking time 35 minutes **serves** 12
per serving 832kJ (198 cal);
6.8g total fat (2.5g saturated fat);
18.6g carbohydrate; 1.2g fibre; medium GI

*You'll probably have to open a 810g
can of whole plums in syrup to get the
required amount for this recipe. You can
serve the remaining plums alongside this
cake, or you can freeze them (in the
syrup) until you wish to use them for
another recipe.*

½ cup (125g) low-fat
  dairy-free spread
1 teaspoon vanilla essence
½ cup (100g) firmly packed
  brown sugar
3 eggs, separated
½ cup (75g) white self-raising flour
½ cup (80g) wholemeal
  self-raising flour
1 teaspoon ground cinnamon
4 whole canned plums in syrup,
  drained, halved, seeded

1 Preheat oven to 180°C/160°C
fan-forced. Grease 20cm ring pan;
line base and sides with baking paper.
2 Using electric mixer, beat spread,
essence, sugar and egg yolks in
small bowl until light and fluffy.
Transfer mixture to medium bowl;
stir in flours and cinnamon.
3 Using electric mixer, beat egg whites
in small bowl until soft peaks form;
gently fold whites into cake batter.
4 Spread batter into pan; place
plums, cut-side down, on top. Bake,
uncovered, about 30 minutes. Stand
10 minutes; turn, top-side up, onto
wire rack to cool. Serve dusted with
icing sugar, if desired.

canned plums generally hold their shape
well when used in baking, and they don't
lose any of their sweet flavour.

chocolate brownie

preparation time 15 minutes
cooking time 25 minutes **makes** 16
per brownie 303kJ (73 cal);
3.8g total fat (0.6g saturated fat);
4.7g carbohydrate; 0.2g fibre; medium GI

2 eggs
⅓ cup (75g) firmly packed
   brown sugar
2 teaspoons instant coffee granules
2 tablespoons cocoa powder
1 tablespoon water
1 tablespoon olive oil
40g low-fat dairy-free spread, melted
¼ cup (40g) wholemeal
   self-raising flour
¼ cup (45g) dark Choc Bits
1 teaspoon cocoa powder, extra
2 teaspoons icing sugar

1 Preheat oven to 180°C/160°C fan-forced. Grease deep 19cm-square pan; line base and sides with baking paper, extending paper 5cm above two opposing sides of pan.
2 Using electric mixer, beat eggs and sugar in small bowl until thick and creamy. Transfer to medium bowl.
3 Meanwhile, blend coffee and cocoa with the water and oil in small bowl until smooth. Stir in spread. Fold cocoa mixture into egg mixture. Fold in flour and Choc Bits; pour mixture into pan.
4 Bake, uncovered, about 25 minutes or until brownie is firm to the touch. Stand 30 minutes; turn onto wire rack. Serve brownie dusted with sifted combined extra cocoa and icing sugar and, if desired, low-fat ice-cream.

wholemeal date loaf

preparation time 20 minutes
cooking time 1 hour **serves** 14
per serving 779kJ (186 cal);
3.2g total fat (0.5g saturated fat);
23.7g carbohydrate; 2.9g fibre; high GI

1 cup (170g) seeded dates, halved
2 tablespoons boiling water
½ teaspoon bicarbonate of soda
60g low-fat dairy-free spread
2 teaspoons finely grated lemon rind
¾ cup (150g) firmly packed
   brown sugar
200g low-fat cottage cheese
2 eggs
2 cups (320g) wholemeal
   self-raising flour
2 tablespoons wheat germ

1 Preheat oven to 160°C/140°C fan-forced. Grease 14cm x 21cm loaf pan; line base and two long sides with baking paper, extending paper 5cm above edges of pan.
2 Combine dates, the water and bicarbonate of soda in small bowl, cover; stand 5 minutes.
3 Using electric mixer, beat spread, rind and sugar in small bowl until light and fluffy. Add cottage cheese; beat until smooth. Add eggs, one at a time; beating until combined.
4 Stir in flour, wheat germ and date mixture; pour into pan.
5 Bake, uncovered, about 1 hour. Stand 10 minutes; turn onto wire rack to cool.

chocolate ricotta tart

preparation time 15 minutes
(plus refrigeration time)
cooking time 35 minutes **serves** 8
per serving 706kJ (169 cal);
6.5g total fat (2.9g saturated fat);
21g carbohydrate; 1.2g fibre; medium GI

¼ cup (35g) white self-raising flour
¼ cup (40g) wholemeal
    self-raising flour
2 tablespoons caster sugar
2 teaspoons cocoa powder
30g low-fat dairy-free spread
2 teaspoons water
1 egg yolk
ricotta filling
150g low-fat ricotta
1 egg
1 egg yolk
¼ cup (70g) low-fat yogurt
¼ cup (55g) caster sugar
2 teaspoons white plain flour
2 tablespoons dark Choc Bits
2 teaspoons coffee-flavoured
    liqueur

1 Grease 18cm-round loose-based flan tin.
2 Process flours, sugar, sifted cocoa and spread until crumbly; add the water and egg yolk, process until ingredients just cling together. Knead dough gently on lightly floured surface until smooth, cover; refrigerate 30 minutes.
3 Preheat oven to 200°C/180°C fan-forced.
4 Press dough into tin; cover with baking paper large enough to extend 5cm over edge, fill with dried beans or rice. Bake, on oven tray, 10 minutes; remove beans and paper. Bake further 5 minutes or until pastry is browned lightly; cool.
5 Reduce oven temperature to 180°C/160°C fan-forced. Pour ricotta filling into pastry case; bake, uncovered, about 20 minutes. Cool; refrigerate until firm.
ricotta filling Using electric mixer, beat ricotta, egg, egg yolk, yogurt, sugar and flour in medium bowl until smooth. Stir in Choc Bits and liqueur.

choc bits are great to use when baking because they hold their shape and add an explosive chocolatey crunch.

apricot upside-down cakes

preparation time 20 minutes
cooking time 20 minutes
makes 12
per cake 554kJ (132 cal);
5.2g total fat (0.6g saturated fat);
18.2g carbohydrate; 1.4g fibre; medium GI

You'll probably have to open a 415g can of apricot halves to get the required amount for this recipe. Serve the remaining apricot halves with the cakes.

1 tablespoon brown sugar
12 canned apricot halves in
    syrup, drained
2 eggs
¾ cup (150g) firmly packed
    brown sugar, extra
¾ cup (90g) almond meal
1 teaspoon vanilla essence
⅓ cup (50g) wholemeal
    self-raising flour
½ cup (125ml) no-fat milk
¼ cup (80g) light apricot
    conserve, warmed

1 Preheat oven to 180°C/160°C fan-forced. Grease 12-hole ⅓ cup (80ml) muffin pan.
2 Sprinkle sugar equally into pan holes; add 1 apricot half, cut-side down, to each hole.
3 Using electric mixer, beat eggs and extra sugar in medium bowl until light and fluffy. Stir in almond meal, essence, flour and milk. Divide mixture among pan holes.
4 Bake about 20 minutes. Stand 5 minutes; turn onto wire rack. Brush apricot conserve over hot cakes. Serve cakes warm or at room temperature.

fig-topped cheesecake

preparation time 25 minutes
(plus refrigeration time) **serves** 16
per serving 387kJ (92 cal);
3.6g total fat (1.3g saturated fat);
6.6g carbohydrate; 0.2g fibre; medium GI

"Nice" biscuits make a perfect base for this yummy cheesecake.

11 plain sweet biscuits (135g)
2 teaspoons gelatine
2 tablespoons water
200g low-fat yogurt
250g light cream cheese, softened
¼ cup (90g) honey
1 teaspoon ground cardamom
2 fresh figs (120g), cut into wedges

1 Grease deep 19cm-square cake pan; line base and sides with baking paper, extending paper 5cm above two opposing sides of pan.
2 Place biscuits in pan; trim to cover base in a single layer.
3 Sprinkle gelatine over the water in small heatproof jug; place jug in small pan of simmering water, stir until gelatine dissolves. Cool 5 minutes.
4 Using electric mixer, beat yogurt and cream cheese in small bowl until smooth. Stir in honey and cardamom then gelatine mixture; pour into pan. Cover; refrigerate about 4 hours or until set. Serve cheesecake topped with fig wedges.

moist orange cake

preparation time 15 minutes
cooking time 20 minutes
(plus standing time)
serves 12
per serving 755kJ (180 cal);
5.3g total fat (0.8g saturated fat);
30.7g carbohydrate; 2.5g fibre; medium GI

4 large oranges (1.2kg)
60g low-fat dairy-free spread
1 cup (220g) caster sugar
2 eggs
⅓ cup (40g) almond meal
1 cup (160g) wholemeal
   self-raising flour
2 tablespoons no-fat soy milk

1 Preheat oven to 160°C/140°C fan-forced. Grease shallow 23cm-round cake pan; line base and side with baking paper.

2 Finely grate ½ teaspoon of rind from 1 orange; slice 1 tablespoon of thin strips of rind from same orange. Reserve rinds. Squeeze the peeled orange; reserve ⅔ cup (160ml) juice. Peel remaining 3 oranges; separate into segments. Reserve segments.

3 Using electric mixer, beat spread, ⅓ cup of the sugar and the finely grated rind in small bowl until pale and creamy. Add eggs; beat until combined. Add almond meal, flour, 1 tablespoon of the orange juice and milk; stir to combine. Spread batter into pan. Bake, uncovered, about 20 minutes.

4 Meanwhile, combine remaining juice and remaining sugar in small saucepan over heat, without boiling, until sugar dissolves; bring to a boil. Add reserved rind strips; simmer, uncovered, about 3 minutes or until syrup thickens slightly.

5 Remove cake from oven. Stand 5 minutes; turn onto wire rack. Using skewer, pierce cake several times; brush with ¼ cup of the hot syrup. Serve cake with reserved orange segments and remaining syrup.

raspberry yogurt cake

preparation time 30 minutes
cooking time 1 hour 5 minutes
serves 12
per serving 572kJ (137 cal);
1.5g total fat (0.8g saturated fat);
28g carbohydrate; 2.3g fibre; medium GI

Raspberries are a great addition to this delicious cake with their delicate flavour and tender texture.

½ cup (125g) low-fat
   dairy-free spread
¾ cup (165g) firmly packed
   brown sugar
2 eggs
1¼ cups (200g) wholemeal
   self-raising flour
½ cup (140g) low-fat yogurt
100g frozen raspberries
cream-cheese frosting
80g light cream cheese, softened
⅓ cup (55g) icing sugar
1 teaspoon lemon juice

1 Preheat oven to 180°C/160°C fan-forced. Grease 14cm x 21cm loaf pan; line base and two long sides with baking paper, extending paper 5cm above edges.
2 Using electric mixer, beat spread and sugar in medium bowl until light and fluffy. Add eggs, one at a time, beating until just combined.
3 Transfer mixture to medium bowl; stir in flour, yogurt and raspberries. Spread mixture into pan.
4 Bake, uncovered, about 1 hour 5 minutes. Stand 10 minutes, turn cake, top-side up, onto wire to cool. Place cake on serving plate; using spatula, spread cake with cream-cheese frosting.
cream-cheese frosting Whisk ingredients in small bowl until smooth.

yogurt and mango jelly

preparation time 5 minutes
(plus refrigeration time)
serves 6
per serving 720kJ (172 cal);
1g total fat (0.5g saturated fat);
36.3g carbohydrate; 2.6g fibre; low GI

We used golden kiwifruit in this recipe. You need 2 passionfruit for this recipe.

85g packet mango jelly crystals
1 cup (250ml) boiling water
2 x 200g cartons low-fat
   five-fruits yogurt
1 medium mango (430g),
   chopped finely
1 medium banana (200g),
   sliced thinly
1 medium kiwifruit (85g), halved,
   sliced thinly
2 tablespoons passionfruit pulp

1 Stir jelly crystals with the water in small heatproof bowl until dissolved; refrigerate about 20 minutes or until cold (do not allow to set).
2 Add yogurt and mango to jelly; stir to combine. Divide jelly mixture among six 1-cup (250ml) serving glasses. Cover; refrigerate about 2 hours or until set.
3 Just before serving, top each jelly with equal amounts of banana, kiwifruit and passionfruit.

vanilla bean ice-cream with espresso sauce

preparation time 10 minutes
cooking time 15 minutes
(plus standing, cooling and freezing time)
serves 4
per serving 965kJ (231 cal);
7g total fat (3.7g saturated fat);
35.6g carbohydrate; 0g fibre; medium GI

1 vanilla bean
1 cup (250ml) light evaporated milk
⅓ cup (80ml) light cream
2 egg yolks
½ cup (110g) caster sugar
½ cup (125ml) boiling water
1 tablespoon ground espresso
coffee beans

1 Split vanilla bean lengthways; scrape seeds into small saucepan. Add vanilla bean, evaporated milk and cream; bring to a boil. Remove from heat, cover; stand 20 minutes. Discard vanilla bean.

2 Meanwhile, using electric mixer, beat egg yolks and sugar in small bowl until thick and creamy; gradually stir in vanilla mixture.

3 Return mixture to same pan; cook, stirring, over low heat, about 15 minutes or until mixture thickens slightly (do not allow to boil).

4 Strain ice-cream mixture into 20cm x 30cm lamington pan, cover surface with foil; cool to room temperature. Freeze until almost set.

5 Place ice-cream in large bowl; chop coarsely. Using electric mixer, beat ice-cream until smooth. Pour into 14cm x 21cm loaf pan, cover; freeze until ice-cream is firm.

6 Just before serving, combine the water and coffee in coffee plunger; stand 2 minutes before plunging. Cool 5 minutes before serving over ice-cream.

glossary

all-bran low-fat, high-fibre breakfast cereal based on wheat bran.

almonds

    blanched skins removed.
    flaked paper-thin slices.
    meal also known as finely ground almonds; powdered to a flour-like texture and used as a thickening agent or in baking.
    slivered lengthways-cut pieces.

apple cider a beverage made by pressing the juice from apples; sold as fresh "sweet" cider and "hard" cider (after fermentation). Alcoholic content ranges widely.

baking powder a raising agent consisting mainly of two parts cream of tartar to one part bicarbonate of soda (baking soda).

barley a nutritious grain used in soups and stews, as well as in whisky and beer making. Pearl barley has had the husk discarded and been hulled and polished, much the same as rice.

barley flakes also known as rolled barley, and steamed and rolled barley; flattened grains produced by steaming the grain then rolling it into flakes.

beef

    eye fillet tenderloin; good for roasting and barbecuing.
    mince also known as ground beef.
    rump steak boneless tender cut; rib eye, sirloin and fillet steak are all suitable substitutes.

beetroot also known as red beets or beets; firm, round root vegetable.

bicarbonate of soda also known as baking or carb soda.

biscuits also known as cookies.

    nice an uniced, plain sweet biscuit topped with a sprinkle of sugar.
    sweet any plain sweet biscuit can be used as long as they are neither filled nor iced.

black mustard seeds also known as brown mustard seeds; more pungent than the white (or yellow) seeds used in most prepared mustards.

buk choy also known as bak choy, pak choy, chinese white cabbage and chinese chard; has a mild mustard taste. Baby buk choy is smaller and more tender; it is often cooked whole.

breadcrumbs

    packaged fine-textured, crunchy, purchased, white breadcrumbs.
    stale one- or two-day-old bread made into crumbs by grating, blending or processing.

broccolini a cross between broccoli and chinese kale; is milder and sweeter than broccoli. Has a long stem topped by a loose floret; is completely edible. Substitute gai lan (chinese broccoli) or broccoli if you are unable to find it.

buckwheat a herb in the same plant family as rhubarb; not a cereal so is gluten free. Available as flour (used to make blini and soba), coarsely ground, or whole and hulled (groats). Kasha, roasted buckwheat groats, is cooked like rice and has a nutty toasty flavour.

burghul also known as bulghur wheat. Hulled steamed wheat kernels that, once dried, are crushed into various-sized grains; not the same as cracked wheat. Used in Middle-Eastern dishes such as kibbeh and tabbouleh.

buttermilk sold alongside fresh milk products in supermarkets; despite the implication of its name, is low in fat. Commercially made by a method similar to yogurt. A good low-fat substitution for dairy products such as cream or sour cream; good in baking, sauces and salad dressings.

cannellini bean small, dried white bean similar in appearance and taste to great northern, navy or haricot beans. Sometimes sold as butter beans.

capsicum also known as bell pepper or, simply, pepper. Can be red, green, yellow, orange or purplish black. Discard seeds and membranes before use.

cardamom can be purchased in pod, seed or ground form. Has a distinctive aromatic, sweetly rich flavour and is one of the world's most expensive spices.

celeriac also known as celery root or celery knob; a tuberous root vegetable with brown skin, white flesh and a celery-like flavour.

cheese

    cheddar a semi-hard cow-milk cheese. We used a low-fat variety with a fat content of not more than 7g per 25g.

cream commonly known as Philly or Philadelphia; a mild-flavoured fresh cheese made of cow milk. It is an acid curd cheese that needs a starter culture of bacteria. We used one with 21g fat per 100g.

    mozzarella this soft, spun-curd cheese was traditionally made from water buffalo milk. Cow-milk versions of this product are now available. We used one with 17.5g fat per 100g.
    ricotta a low-fat, fresh unripened cheese with 3g fat per 100g.

chickpeas also called garbanzos, hummus or channa; an irregularly round, sandy-coloured legume used extensively in Mediterranean cooking.

choy sum also known as flowering buk choy or flowering white cabbage.

cooking-oil spray we used a cholesterol-free cooking spray made from canola oil.

cornflour also known as cornstarch; used as a thickening agent.

cornmeal ground dried corn (maize); available in different textures.

couscous a fine, grain-like cereal product, originally from North Africa; made from semolina.

eggplant also known as aubergine.

extracts also known as essences; the by-product of distillation of plants.

flour

    buckwheat although not a true cereal, flour is made from its seeds. Available from health food stores.
    self-raising wholemeal or plain flour combined with baking powder in the proportion of 1 cup flour to 2 teaspoons baking powder.
    soy made from ground soybeans.
    white plain an all-purpose flour, made from wheat.

gai lan also known as chinese broccoli; stems used more than its coarse leaves.

ginger also known as green or root ginger; the thick gnarled root of a tropical plant. Can be kept, peeled, covered with dry sherry in a jar and refrigerated, or frozen in an airtight container.

golden syrup by-product of refined sugarcane; pure maple syrup or honey can be substituted.

ham we used light ham with a fat content of 2.3g per 100g, about half that of regular ham.

kasha also known as roasted buckwheat groats; has a nutty, richly toasty flavour and can be served like polenta, couscous or rice with a meat casserole or roast.

kecap manis an Indonesian sweet, thick soy sauce that has sugar and spices added.

kumara the Polynesian name of orange-fleshed sweet potato, often confused with yam.

lavash flat, unleavened bread, originally from the Mediterranean.

lemon grass a tall, clumping, lemon-smelling and -tasting, sharp-edged grass; the white lower part of each stem is chopped and used in Asian cooking or for tea.

lentils dried pulses often identified by and named after their colour (red, brown or yellow); also known as dhal.

light sour cream we used a low-fat sour cream having a fat content of 18.5g per 100g.

linguine long, narrow pasta often thought of as a flat spaghetti.

low-fat cream we used cream having a fat content of 18%.

low-fat dairy-free spread we used Diet Becel, a commercial product having a fat content of 2.4g per 5g of spread (47g of fat per 100g of spread).

low-fat mayonnaise we used cholesterol-free mayonnaise having less than 3g fat per 100g.

low-fat thickened cream we used cream having a fat content of 18%.

low-fat yogurt we used yogurt having a fat content of less than 0.2%.

maple syrup distilled sap of the maple tree. Maple-favoured syrup is made from cane sugar and artificial maple flavouring and is not a substitute for the real thing.

mesclun mixed baby salad leaves also sold as salad mix or gourmet salad mix; a mixture of assorted young lettuce and other green leaves, including mizuna, baby spinach leaves and curly endive.

mince meat also known as ground meat, as in beef, pork and chicken.

mushrooms

    button small, cultivated white mushrooms having a delicate, subtle flavour.

    swiss brown light- to dark-brown mushrooms with full-bodied flavour. Button or cup mushrooms can be substituted.

no-fat milk we used milk with a fat content of 0.15% or lower.

noodles

    fresh rice thick, wide, almost white in colour; made from rice and vegetable oil. Must be covered with boiling water to remove starch and excess oil before using in soups and stir-fries.

    hokkien also known as stir-fry noodles; fresh wheat noodles resembling thick, yellow-brown spaghetti and needing no pre-cooking before use.

    rice stick a dried noodle, available flat and wide or very thin; made from rice flour and water.

    rice vermicelli also known as rice-flour noodles and rice-stick noodles; made from ground rice. Sold dried, are best either deep-fried, or soaked then stir-fried or used in soups.

onion

    brown and white these are interchangeable. Their pungent flesh adds flavour to a vast range of dishes.

    green also known as scallion or, incorrectly, shallot; an immature onion picked before the bulb has formed, having a long, bright-green edible stalk.

    red also known as red spanish, spanish or bermuda onion; a sweet, large, purple-red onion that is particularly good eaten raw in salads.

paprika ground, dried red capsicum (bell pepper), available sweet or hot.

parsley, flat-leaf also known as continental parsley or italian parsley.

passionfruit also known as granadilla. A small tropical fruit, native to Brazil; has a tough dark-purple skin surrounding edible black sweet-sour seeds.

pecan nut buttery, golden-brown and rich. Good in savoury as well as sweet dishes; especially good in salads.

pepitas the dried seeds of a pumpkin.

pide also known as turkish bread, comes in long (about 45cm) flat loaves as well as individual rounds. Made from wheat flour and sprinkled with sesame or black onion seeds.

pitta also spelled pita and known as lebanese bread, this wheat-flour pocket bread is sold in large, flat pieces that separate easily into two thin rounds. Also available in small thick pieces called pocket pitta.

polenta a flour-like cereal made of ground corn (maize); also known as cornmeal. Also the name of the dish made from it.

raisins large, dried sweet grapes.

rhubarb a vegetable related to sorrel; only the firm, reddish stems are eaten.

rice

    arborio small, round-grain rice well-suited to absorb a large amount of liquid; especially suitable for making risottos.

    basmati a white fragrant long-grain rice. It should be washed several times before cooking.

    doongara a long-grain rice having a lower GI (glycaemic index) rating than many other rice varieties; is more slowly absorbed into the blood stream, so it helps provide sustained energy release.

    jasmine a fragrant long-grain rice; white rice can be substituted, but will not taste the same.

    white a hulled and polished rice; can be short-or long-grained.

rice paper sheets made from rice paste and stamped into rounds with a woven pattern. Stores well at room temperature although are quite brittle and break easily. Dipped momentarily in water, they become pliable wrappers for fried food and for wrapping around fresh vegetables.

risoni also known as risi; small rice-shaped pasta very similar to another small pasta, orzo.

rocket also known as arugula, rugula or rucola; a peppery-tasting green leaf that can be used similarly to baby spinach leaves. Can be cooked or eaten raw in salads. Baby rocket leaves are both smaller and less peppery.

rolled grains includes rice, barley, oats, rye and triticale; the whole grain has been steamed and flattened – not the quick-cook variety. Available from health food stores and supermarkets.

rosewater extract made from crushed rose petals; used for its aromatic quality in many desserts and sweets.

salted black beans also known as chinese black beans; are fermented and salted soy beans available in cans and jars. Chop before, or mash during, cooking to release flavour.

sauces

> **barbecue** a spicy tomato-based sweet sauce used to marinate or baste, or as an accompaniment.
> **fish** also called nam pla or nuoc nam; made from pulverised salted fermented fish, most often anchovies. Has a pungent smell and strong taste; use sparingly.
> **oyster** a rich, brown sauce made from oysters and their brine, cooked with salt and soy sauce, and thickened with starches.
> **soy** made from fermented soy beans. Many variations are available in most supermarkets; we used a mild Japanese variety.
> **sweet chilli** a relatively mild, thai sauce made from red chillies, sugar, garlic and vinegar.
> **tomato pasta sauce, bottled** prepared sauce available from supermarkets; also known as sugo.

seed tapioca also called sago because it comes from the sago palm pearl; tapioca is from the root of the cassava plant. Available from most health food stores and some supermarkets.

semolina made from durum wheat; milled into various textured granules, all finer than flour. The main ingredient in good pastas and some kinds of gnocchi.

silver beet also known as seakale or swiss chard. A green-leafed vegetable with sturdy celery-like white stems. A member of the beet family, silver beet can be used similarly to spinach.

skewers bamboo or metal skewers can be used. Rub oil onto metal skewers to stop meat sticking. Soak bamboo skewers in water for at least 1 hour before use to prevent splintering and scorching.

snow peas also called mange tout (eat all). Snow pea tendrils are the growing shoots of the plant.

Special K low-fat breakfast cereal based on rice and wheat; good source of calcium and iron.

spinach also known as english spinach and, incorrectly, silver beet.

stock 1 cup (250ml) is equivalent to 1 cup (250ml) water plus 1 crumbled stock cube. It may be more convenient to use stock in tetra paks.

sugar

> **brown** an extremely soft, fine granulated sugar retaining molasses for its characteristic colour and flavour.
> **caster** also known as finely granulated table sugar.
> **icing sugar** also known as confectioners' sugar or powdered sugar; granulated sugar crushed together with a small amount of cornflour added.
> **white** we used coarse granulated table sugar, also known as crystal sugar, unless stated otherwise.

sugar snap peas also known as honey snap peas; fresh small pea that can be eaten whole, pod and all.

sultanas small dried grapes, also known as golden raisins.

sumac a purple-red, astringent spice ground from berries growing on Mediterranean shrubs; adds a tart lemony flavour to dips and goes well with barbecued meat. Available from Middle-Eastern food stores.

sunflower seed kernels kernels from dried, husked sunflower seeds.

taco shells commercially prepared deep-fried corn tortillas folded over to create a container for various fillings.

tamarind paste made from the pods of a tree native to India that contain a sour-sweet pulp that is dried then reconstituted to make the dark, thick paste that adds a tangy astringent taste to curries. It can also be used in marinades and bastes for meats.

tikka masala curry paste literally meaning blended spices; a masala can be whole spices, a paste or a powder, and can include herbs as well as spices and other seasonings.

tofu also known as bean curd; an off-white, custard-like product made from the milk of crushed soy beans. Available fresh as soft or firm, and processed as fried or pressed dried sheets. Silken tofu refers to the method by which it is made, strained through silk.

tortilla unleavened bread sold frozen, fresh or vacuum-packed; made from either wheat flour or corn (maize meal).

tomato

> **cherry** small, round tomatoes also known as tiny tim or tom thumb.
> **egg** also called plum or roma; are smallish oval-shaped tomatoes.

triticale a nutritious hybrid of wheat (triticum) and rye (secale), which contains more protein and less gluten than wheat and has a nutty, sweet flavour. Available in whole grain, flour and flakes.

unprocessed bran made from the outer layer of a cereal – most often the husks of wheat, rice or oats.

vanilla bean dried, long, thin pod from a tropical orchid; the tiny black seeds inside the bean are used to impart a vanilla flavour in baking and desserts. Place a whole bean in a container of sugar to make the vanilla sugar called for in recipes.

vietnamese mint not actually a mint at all, this narrow-leafed, pungent herb is also known as cambodian mint and laksa leaf (daun laksa).

vinegar

> **balsamic** made from a regional wine of white Trebbiano grapes specially processed then aged in antique wooden casks to give the exquisite pungent flavour.
> **red wine** based on fermented red wine.
> **white wine** made from fermented white wine.

wheat germ small creamy flakes milled from the embryo of the berry.

wombok also known as chinese or peking cabbage. Elongated in shape with pale green, crinkly leaves, this is the most common cabbage in South-East Asia.

zucchini also known as courgette; small green, yellow or white vegetable belonging to the squash family.

conversion chart

MEASURES

One Australian metric measuring cup holds approximately 250ml; one Australian metric tablespoon holds 20ml; one Australian metric teaspoon holds 5ml.

The difference between one country's measuring cups and another's is within a two- or three-teaspoon variance, and will not affect your cooking results. North America, New Zealand and the United Kingdom use a 15ml tablespoon.

All cup and spoon measurements are level. The most accurate way of measuring dry ingredients is to weigh them. When measuring liquids, use a clear glass or plastic jug with the metric markings.

We use large eggs with an average weight of 60g.

DRY MEASURES

METRIC	IMPERIAL
15g	½oz
30g	1oz
60g	2oz
90g	3oz
125g	4oz (¼lb)
155g	5oz
185g	6oz
220g	7oz
250g	8oz (½lb)
280g	9oz
315g	10oz
345g	11oz
375g	12oz (¾lb)
410g	13oz
440g	14oz
470g	15oz
500g	16oz (1lb)
750g	24oz (1½lb)
1kg	32oz (2lb)

LIQUID MEASURES

METRIC	IMPERIAL
30ml	1 fluid oz
60ml	2 fluid oz
100ml	3 fluid oz
125ml	4 fluid oz
150ml	5 fluid oz (¼ pint/1 gill)
190ml	6 fluid oz
250ml	8 fluid oz
300ml	10 fluid oz (½ pint)
500ml	16 fluid oz
600ml	20 fluid oz (1 pint)
1000ml (1 litre)	1¾ pints

LENGTH MEASURES

METRIC	IMPERIAL
3mm	⅛in
6mm	¼in
1cm	½in
2cm	¾in
2.5cm	1in
5cm	2in
6cm	2½in
8cm	3in
10cm	4in
13cm	5in
15cm	6in
18cm	7in
20cm	8in
23cm	9in
25cm	10in
28cm	11in
30cm	12in (1ft)

OVEN TEMPERATURES

These oven temperatures are only a guide for conventional ovens. For fan-forced ovens, check the manufacturer's manual.

	°C (CELSIUS)	°F (FAHRENHEIT)	GAS MARK
Very slow	120	250	½
Slow	150	275-300	1-2
Moderately slow	160	325	3
Moderate	180	350-375	4-5
Moderately hot	200	400	6
Hot	220	425-450	7-8
Very hot	240	475	9

index

If you like this cookbook, you'll love these...

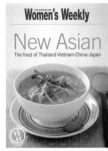

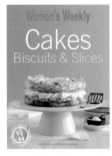

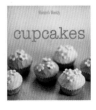

These are just a small selection of titles available in
The Australian Women's Weekly range on sale at selected
newsagents, supermarkets or online at www.acpbooks.com.au

also available in bookstores...

TEST KITCHEN
Food director Pamela Clark
Associate food editor Alexandra Somerville
Home economists Kelli Ann, Sammie Coryton, Kelly Cruickshanks, Cathie Lonnie, Naomi Scesny, Jeanette Seamons, Alison Webb, Danielle West

ACP BOOKS
General manager Christine Whiston
Editorial director Susan Tomnay
Creative director Hieu Chi Nguyen
Senior editors Julie Collard, Lynda Wilton
Designer Hannah Blackmore
Director of sales Brian Cearnes
Marketing manager Bridget Cody
Business analyst Ashley Davies
Operations manager David Scotto
International rights enquires Laura Bamford
lbamford@acpuk.com

ACP Books are published by ACP Magazines
a division of PBL Media Pty Limited
Group publisher, Women's lifestyle
Pat Ingram
Director of sales, Women's lifestyle
Lynette Phillips
Commercial manager, Women's lifestyle
Seymour Cohen
Marketing director, Women's lifestyle
Matthew Dominello
Public relations manager, Women's lifestyle
Hannah Deveraux
Creative director, Events, Women's lifestyle
Luke Bonnano
Research Director, Women's lifestyle
Justin Stone
ACP Magazines, Chief Executive officer
Scott Lorson
PBL Media, Chief Executive officer
Ian Law

Produced by ACP Books, Sydney.
Published by ACP Books, a division of
ACP Magazines Ltd, 54 Park St, Sydney;
GPO Box 4088, Sydney, NSW 2001.
phone (02) 9282 8618 fax (02) 9267 9438.
acpbooks@acpmagazines.com.au
www.acpbooks.com.au
Printed by Dai Nippon in Korea.

Australia Distributed by Network Services,
phone +61 2 9282 8777 fax +61 2 9264 3278
networkweb@networkservicescompany.com.au
United Kingdom Distributed by Australian
Consolidated Press (UK),
phone (01604) 642 200 fax (01604) 642 300
books@acpuk.com
New Zealand Distributed by Netlink
Distribution Company,
phone (9) 366 9966 ask@ndc.co.nz
South Africa Distributed by PSD Promotions,
phone (27 11) 392 6065/6/7
fax (27 11) 392 6079/80
orders@psdprom.co.za

Clark, Pamela.
The Australian Women's Weekly
Wellbeing The Diabetes Cookbook.
Includes index.
ISBN 978-1-86396-616-0.
1. Diabetes – diet therapy – Recipes.
I. Title: Australian Women's Weekly
641.56314
© ACP Magazines Ltd 2006
ABN 18 053 273 546
This publication is copyright. No part of it may be
reproduced or transmitted in any form without the
written permission of the publishers.
First published in 2003 as Low-fat Food for Life.
Revised & updated 2006. Reprinted 2007.
To order books,
phone 136 116 (within Australia).
Send recipe enquiries to:
recipeenquiries@acpmagazines.com.au